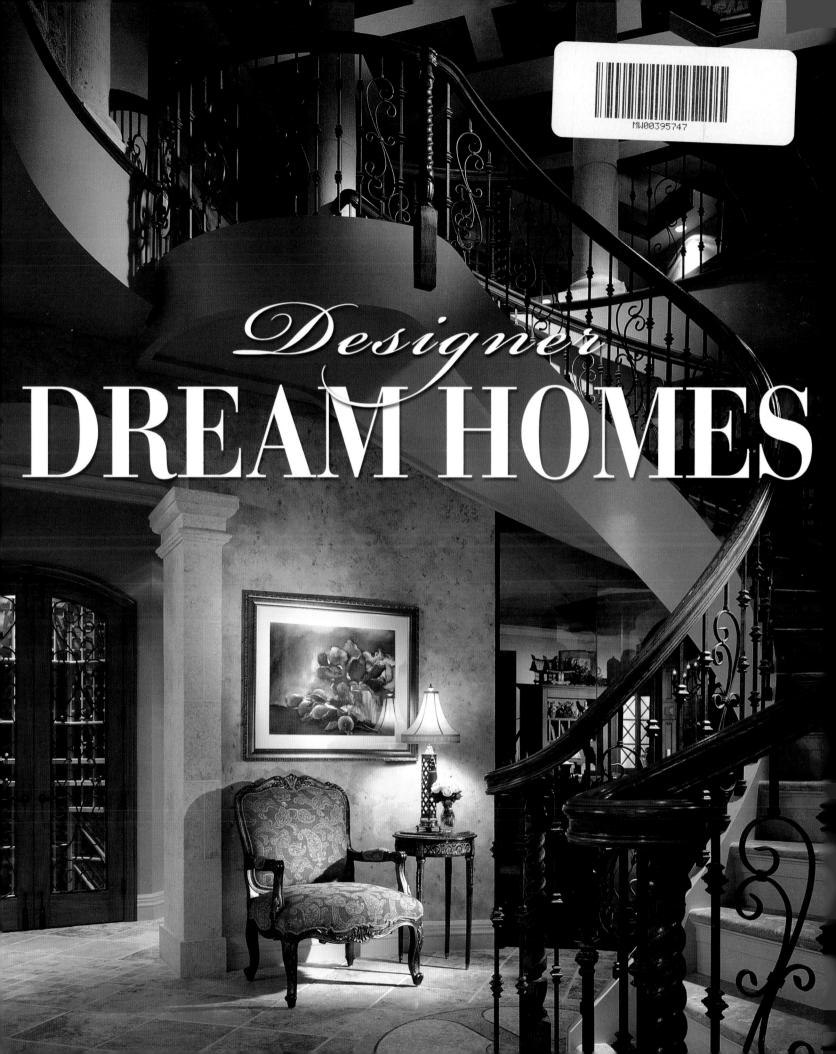

Designer
DREAM HOMES

PRESIDENT
Angela Santerini

PUBLISHER
Dominic Foley

EDITOR
Jennifer Baker

CONTRIBUTING EDITORS
Darlene Fuhst, Heidi Haunold, Krista Mysock, Laura Segers

CONTRIBUTING WRITERS
Jennifer Bacon, Jeffrey deRoulet, Laura Hurst Brown,
Sarah Hockman, Alan Lopuszynski, Matt McGarry, Paula Powers,
Laura Segers, Clare Ulik

GRAPHIC ARTISTS
Kim Campeau, Emily Sessa, Bishana Shipp,
Joshua Thomas, Diane Zwack

ILLUSTRATORS
Architectural Art, Allen Bennetts, Concept Visualization, Inc.,
Greg Havens, Holzhauer, Inc., Dave Jenkins,
Kurt Kauss, Barry Nathan

PHOTOGRAPHERS
Warren Bond, Everett & Soulé, Dan Forer, Get Decorating,
Tom Harper, Walter Kirk, Gregg Krogstad, Joseph Lapeyra,
McManus Photo, John Riley, Kim Sargent, Matthew Scott,
Laurence Taylor, Happy Terrebone, Doug Thompson,
Oscar Thompson, CJ Walker, John G. Wilbanks, Bryan Willy

A DESIGNS DIRECT PUBLISHING BOOK
Printed by: Toppan Printing Co., Hong Kong
First Printing: February 2007
10 9 8 7 6 5 4 3 2 1

ISBN softcover: (10-digit) 1-932553-24-X
(13-digit) 978-1-932553-24-6

Cedar Court -

DONALD A. GARDNER ARCHITECTS -

See page 68

Chatham -

CORNERSTONE DESIGNS - See page 8

Estate COLLECTION

PHOTO FEATURES

ESTATE PLAN PAGES

European COLLECTION

PHOTO FEATURES

EUROPEAN PLAN PAGES

American CLASSICS

PHOTO FEATURES

AMERICAN PLAN PAGES

Kinsey -
SATER DESIGN COLLECTION -
See page 90

Vacation COLLECTION

COTTAGE

PHOTO FEATURES

Vacation COLLECTION

MOUNTAIN

PHOTO FEATURES

VACATION PLAN PAGES

ORDER PAGES

Estate Collection

Chatham
CORNERSTONE DESIGNS - See page 8

Chatham - **REAR EXTERIOR**

True luxury does not need to be defined. Instead, it defines itself.

From the dramatic, arched entryways of stone

to the majestic columns that define them, these extraordinary estate plans

feature gorgeous, striking details throughout. Sprawling, open floor plans

where leisure rooms flow into gourmet kitchens; where a two-story foyer

opens, magnificently, into both formal dining and living rooms;

where double-sided fireplaces and retreating-glass walls provide style, grace

and innovation; and where lavish master suites offer privacy,

silence and rest. Around each corner, down every impressive hallway, there

is something exciting — luxurious — to be found here as the home

extends outside its walls to the gardens, porches, pools

and verandas beyond.

Casa Bellisima

SATER DESIGN COLLECTION - See page 24

Chatham

© CORNERSTONE DESIGNS, LLC

PLAN# DHCS01-M7550A4S-0   **1-866-525-9374**

Embodying the essence of seaboard charm, the *Chatham's* shingle-style gables, gambrels, columns, turrets, balconies and verandas entice visitors to approach.

One is immediately drawn from the traditional foyer into the spectacular, grand circular rotunda with its domed stained-glass ceiling and compass rose floor. The two-story great room beyond, with its curved-bay window, anchors the expansive family living area.

Formal living and dining rooms provide for grand entertaining, while the intimate library and study allow for quiet activities. Service spaces including a butler, mud room with elevator, and back stair enhance the home's functionality.

The master suite is a magnificent private retreat, while the children's suites are highlighted by playful and unique spaces. A home theater, game room, laundry and crafts room round out the upper floor.

ROTUNDA STAIRS — Topped with a luxurious Tiffany art glass dome and chandelier, the center stair rotunda is the home's dramatic focal point.

KITCHEN — A gourmet's dream, the grand kitchen features every modern convenience in a spacious layout designed for multiple chefs and culinary entertaining. The coffered-beam ceiling, painted cabinets and dark-stained island create a warm, inviting feel.

FAMILY ROOM — The round window bay of the spectacular two-story family room is a great spot for cozy armchairs or a baby grand piano. Extensive use of stained casework provides warmth and intimate scale in such a grand space. The wood-framed opening to the nook features a low divider just right for flower displays, knick-knacks and family photos.

DINING ROOM — The dining room's French doors, triple-coffered ceiling, painted wainscoting and crown moldings create an atmosphere of period luxury.

HIS-AND-HER STUDIES — The wood-paneled study and library make a flexible home office suite for one or two. The fireplace, window bay and private arbor promote reflection and relaxation.

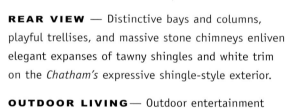

REAR VIEW — Distinctive bays and columns, playful trellises, and massive stone chimneys enliven elegant expanses of tawny shingles and white trim on the *Chatham's* expressive shingle-style exterior.

OUTDOOR LIVING — Outdoor entertainment reigns supreme on the octagonal covered patio. With its built-in barbecue and stone fireplace, you might never want to come back inside!

MASTER BEDROOM & BATH — The tranquil nature of the master suite's sleeping area contrasts with the sunroom-like feel of the raised sitting area, providing an attractive and secluded multi-use owner's refuge.

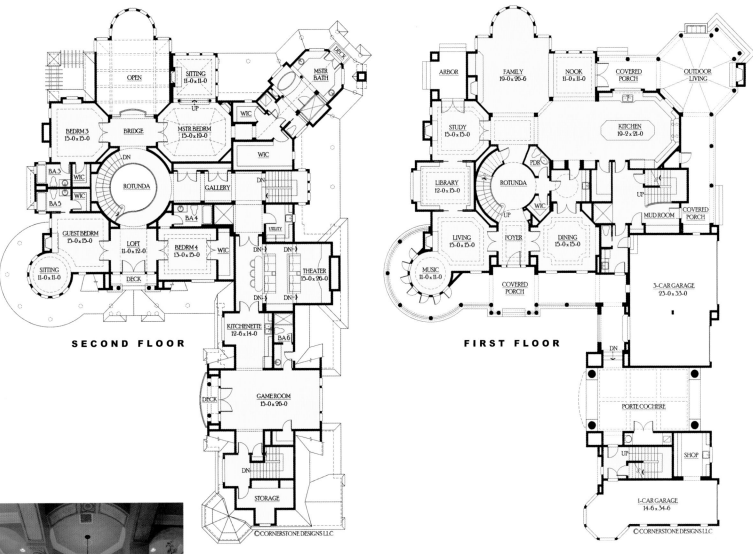

SECOND FLOOR

FIRST FLOOR

©CORNERSTONE DESIGNS LLC

©CORNERSTONE DESIGNS LLC

MASTER BATH — Combining five-star luxury and practical comforts, the master bath's columned soaking tub, spacious double closets and vanities, stepped ceiling, balcony and stacked washer-dryer has it all.

GUEST ROOM — The spacious guest suite's domed sitting turret, fireplace, private bath and walk-in closet could entice some guests to overstay their welcome.

TO ORDER CALL: 1-866-525-9374		PLAN#:DHCS01-M7550A4S-0			*Chatham*			
TOTAL LIVING	FIRST FLOOR	SECOND FLOOR	BED	BATH	WIDTH	DEPTH	FOUNDATION	PRICE CODE
7900 sq. ft.	3400 sq. ft.	4500 sq. ft.	5	5-1/2	95'4"	135'0"	Crawl Space	0

Home photographed may differ from construction documents.

© CORNERSTONE DESIGNS, LLC

PLAN# DHCS01-M7950A2F2RD-0   1-866-525-9374

Inspired by the villas of Tuscany, this timeless shingle-style estate's five structures are joined by trellised arbors and sheltering roofs. Its traditional forms delightfully contrast with floor plans designed for active lifestyles.

The entry opens to a soaring great hall with a grand stair, fireplace and overlook balcony. A central skylight floods the center of the home with sunlight, drawing attention to the sculptural ceilings. A false bookcase in the oval office hides a spiral stair to the wine cellar below.

Full-width folding-glass doors join the informal living areas with the pool terrace, creating a great entertainment space. The versatile cabana doubles as a mother-in-law apartment. The enormous craft room fulfills every home management need. The upstairs combines luxury and privacy for the owners with fun and play for the children.

GREAT HALL — A grand formal staircase soars past the arched central window of the double-height Great Hall, creating a dramatic and acoustically powerful setting for a grand piano.

KITCHEN — Organized around a huge two-level island, the gourmet kitchen is a chef's fantasy come true. Dark-stained floors and painted cabinets contrast with elegant tile and marble surfaces and a dark-beamed ceiling to create a visually stunning and ergonomically effective workspace.

DINING ROOM — Sharing the dramatic space of the Great Hall, the dining room is defined by boldly trimmed columns, arches and coffered ceilings. A bayed window seat provides an intimate touch.

GREAT ROOM — Deep-set arches and a recessed fireplace trimmed with elegant moldings set the mood for the luxurious great room. The curved stone hearth and painted wood mantel echo the arched balcony gently cantilevered into the dramatic double-height space above.

OVAL OFFICE — Designed for a Commander-in-Chief, the Oval Office is a center of power, full of rich details including a fireplace, bowed window and a private lounge. Behind a secret hinged bookcase is the man cave retreat that lies below.

REAR VIEW — A symphony of shingles, trellises and trim, the residence and cabana create a classic composition. Broad folding-glass doors links the indoor spaces to the grand pool terrace.

MASTER BATH — The master bath is like having a luxury spa at home, with a huge double-entry glass shower, his-and-her vanities and a claw-foot tub overlooking a veranda. The huge dressing room opens to a private exercise area.

MASTER BEDROOM — The exquisite master bedroom is sited for seclusion at one side of the upper floor, featuring elegant ceiling details and a broad sitting bay. A see-thru fireplace, art niches and a private veranda create a restful retreat.

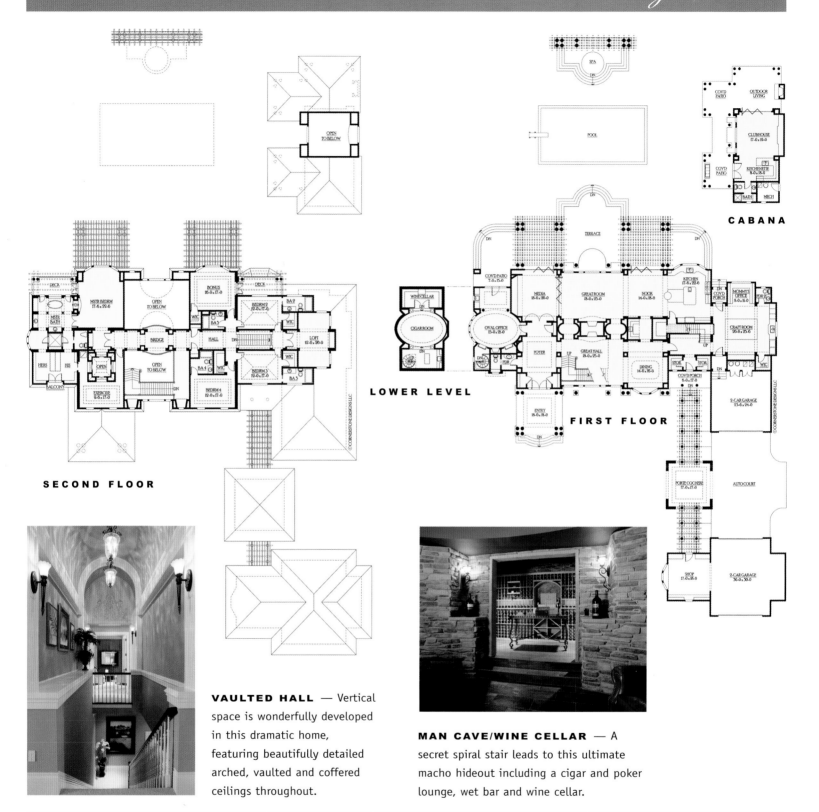

CABANA

LOWER LEVEL

FIRST FLOOR

SECOND FLOOR

VAULTED HALL — Vertical space is wonderfully developed in this dramatic home, featuring beautifully detailed arched, vaulted and coffered ceilings throughout.

MAN CAVE/WINE CELLAR — A secret spiral stair leads to this ultimate macho hideout including a cigar and poker lounge, wet bar and wine cellar.

TO ORDER CALL: 1-866-525-9374	PLAN#:DHCS01- M7950A2F2RD-0	Water's Edge Retreat							
TOTAL LIVING	**FIRST FLOOR**	**SECOND FLOOR**	**LOWER/ CABANA**	**BED**	**BATH**	**WIDTH**	**DEPTH**	**FOUNDATION**	**PRICE CODE**
9820 sq. ft.	4832 sq. ft.	3758 sq. ft.	590/640 sq. ft.	4	6F/2H	125'6"	94'0"	Crawl Space	0

Home photographed may differ from construction documents.

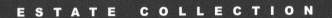

ESTATE COLLECTION

Wedgewood

© 1999 DONALD A. GARDNER

PLAN#   DHDG01-806   **1-866-525-9374**

This custom designed estate elegantly combines stone and stucco, arched windows and stunning exterior details under its formidable hip roof. A home that lacks for nothing, the *Wedgewood* is full of luxuries. The two-story foyer is impressive with its grand staircase, tray ceiling and overlooking balcony. Equally remarkable is the generous living room with fireplace and coffered two-story ceiling. The kitchen, breakfast bay and family room with fireplace are all open to one another for a comfortable, casual atmosphere.

The first-floor master suite indulges with numerous closets, a dressing area and a fabulous bath. Upstairs, tray ceilings top four more bedrooms; three have walk-in closets; two have private baths.

The three-car garage boasts additional storage and a bonus room above.

LIVING ROOM — An arched entry into the living room creates an impressive and formal entrance.

KITCHEN — Completely open, the kitchen and breakfast nook overflow into one another and provide an easy transition into the family and living rooms.

FAMILY ROOM — The family room's stone fireplace adds drama, while French doors bathe the room with sunlight.

LIVING ROOM — The lofty two-story living room features a balcony above as well as beautiful French doors and windows to brighten the room.

BALCONY — Two columns flank the curved balcony that overlooks both the foyer on one side and the formal living room on the other.

REAR VIEW — On the rear exterior, windows and French doors contrast with a keystone arch and deep overhangs.

MASTER BEDROOM — The bayed sitting area provides an extra space for unwinding at the end of a hard day, while granting luxury to the master bedroom.

DINING ROOM — With easy access to the foyer and kitchen, the luxurious dining room is an ideal space for formal meals.

FIRST FLOOR

DECK

BRKFST.
14-0 x 12-8

PORCH

MASTER BED RM.
14-0 x 21-8

fireplace

FAMILY RM.
24-0 x 22-0

LIVING RM.
20-0 x 17-8
(two story ceiling)

fireplace

walk-in closet

seat

KIT.
14-0 x 13-8

balcony above

cl

dressing area

master bath

© 1999 DONALD A. GARDNER
All rights reserved

storage

up

lin.

sto.

walk-in closet

lin.

walk-in closet

shelves

pd. rm.

up

balcony above

UTIL.
10-0 x 8-8

FOYER
20-0 x 7-0
(two story ceiling)

GARAGE
22-0 x 35-4

DINING
14-0 x 16-0

PORCH

LIBRARY
14-0 x 18-0

storage

MASTER BATH — A decorative ceiling, extraordinary chandelier and clawfoot tub create a sophisticated master bath.

SECOND FLOOR

BED RM.
14-0 x 13-4

living room below

BED RM.
14-0 x 14-0

walk-in closet

bath

railing

walk-in closet

bath

balcony

lin.

bath

down

balcony

walk-in closet

bath

BONUS RM.
14-2 x 25-6

attic

railing

cl

cl

foyer below

down

BED RM.
14-0 x 13-8

BED RM.
14-0 x 16-0

attic storage

BREAKFAST NOOK — Hugged by a bay window, the breakfast nook provides panoramic views while enjoying casual meals.

TO ORDER CALL: 1-866-525-9374		PLAN#: DHDG01-806	*Wedgewood*							
TOTAL LIVING	FIRST FLOOR	SECOND FLOOR	BONUS ROOM	BED	BATH	WIDTH	DEPTH	FOUNDATION		PRICE CODE
5158 sq. ft.	3520 sq. ft.	1638 sq. ft.	411 sq. ft.	5	4-1/2	96'6"	72'0"	Crawl Space		K

Home photographed may differ from construction documents.

PLAN# DHDS01-6940   1-866-525-9374

Dramatic rooflines, ornamented windows and a boldly articulated entry combine to create a striking façade. A barrel-vaulted entry opens to spectacular views through the cupola area to the Grand Solana. Massive columns define the varied spaces of the public realm, including a formal dining room, living room and a study secluded behind a two-sided fireplace.

Windows line the rear perimeter of the plan creating a seamless connection to the outdoors. Retreating-glass doors open the leisure room to the Solana and lanai, creating a flexible space for every occasion. Tucked away from the common living areas, the master suite enjoys an entire wing of the home. On the upper level, a winding balcony hall connects a loft area, wet bar, exercise room and media room with a spacious guest suite.

GRAND SOLANA EXTERIOR — Views extend from the foyer to the rear property through a bow window in the grand solana. Overhanging eaves supported by decorative brackets indicate the plan's renaissance roots.

KITCHEN — Stone floors and coffered ceilings define the wide-open spaces of the casual living area. An arching doorway secludes a convenient butler's pantry that links the food-preparation area to a wet bar and wine cellar. Varied architectural forms give shape to this multi-function space, with columns and sculpted arches connecting the rooms.

GRAND SOLANA — Carved Crema Maya stone columns articulate the boundaries of the formal dining room, enhanced by a barrel-vaulted ceiling. The cupola shelters a sitting space in front of the two-story fireplace, while ornate floriated capitals repeat the classical patterns of the surround and frieze.

DINING ROOM — The curved beams of the barrel-vaulted ceiling in the formal dining room are brought into high relief by panels of deep sienna. An interior wall provides an ample canvas for a muted *trompe l'oeil* that deepens the dimensions of the room and lends a sense of tradition to the public realm.

SOLANA — Laden in stone, the *plein air* solana extends the livability of the leisure room and includes a corner fireplace and an alfresco kitchen.

REAR VIEW — Open rooms engage the rear perimeter of the home with wide views and a sense of the outdoors. A series of stepped and square transoms, sculpted arches and curvilinear forms lend depth to the layered elevation.

LOFT — The upper level features a loft with links to the media room, wet bar, sun deck, exercise room and a spacious guest suite. Stepped ceilings, built-in cabinetry and art niches bring Old-World craftsmanship to the modern spaces.

MASTER BEDROOM — A series of square transoms and a stunning mitered-glass window set off the sitting bay of the owners' suite. Soaring ceiling coffers contrast with the linear forms of the space, and heighten the visual dimensions of the room.

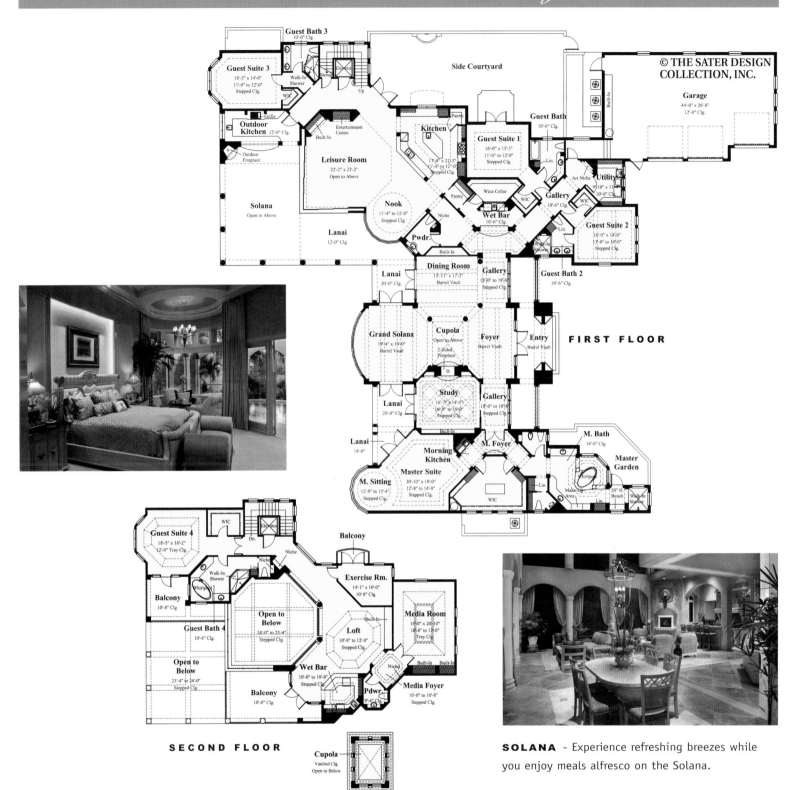

© THE SATER DESIGN COLLECTION, INC.

FIRST FLOOR

SECOND FLOOR

Cupola
Vaulted Clg.
Open to Below

SOLANA - Experience refreshing breezes while you enjoy meals alfresco on the Solana.

TO ORDER CALL: 1-866-525-9374	PLAN#: DHDS01-6940	*Alamosa*

TOTAL LIVING	FIRST FLOOR	SECOND FLOOR	BED	BATH	WIDTH	DEPTH	FOUNDATION	PRICE CODE
8088 sq. ft.	6122 sq. ft.	1966 sq. ft.	5	5F/2H	118'0"	147'10"	Slab	0

Home photographed may differ from construction documents.

Casa Bellisima

© THE SATER DESIGN COLLECTION, INC.

PLAN#   DHDS01-6935   1-866-525-9374

A stunning courtyard leads to the barrel-vaulted covered entry of this view-oriented design. Past the foyer, the formal living room boasts a fireplace, two-story ceiling and a wall of windows and doors connecting to the outdoors. A butler's pantry, wet bar and formal dining room are situated close by. An elegant circular staircase curves upward from the first-floor gallery to a spacious game room with wet bar and a guest suite.

Two more guest suites are found on the left side of the floor plan, as is the kitchen, leisure room and nook, where open spaces are expanded by zero-corner sliding-glass doors that pocket into the walls and open this area onto the veranda. For added privacy, the master suite is located on the opposite wing.

STAIRCASE — Gravity-defying forms define a grand, sweeping staircase that connects the main-level gallery with the game room. A sculpted edge soars above a carved vestibule leading to the wine cellar.

GAME ROOM — A grand rotunda links the main level with the game room, designed as a marvelous getaway for family members and guests. An intricate custom chandelier complements the wrought-iron balusters of the railing that frame and support the circular staircase. A complete wet bar provides refreshments for pool sharks and big-time gamers.

LIVING ROOM — This grand-scale living room impresses immediately upon entry. A striking two-story fireplace framed in carved marble competes with spectacular views beyond a set of glass doors.

KITCHEN — Antique cypress beams hover above the food-preparation area in the kitchen, which boasts granite countertops and new-century appliances. A tumbled-stone stove hood provides an earthy element to this ultra-sophisticated kitchen.

LEISURE ROOM — A built-in, corner entertainment center provides amusement under a diamond-shaped, wood-beamed ceiling. Disappearing sliding-glass walls merge two sides of the leisure room with the veranda for seamless indoor-outdoor flow.

VERANDA — An arcade of arches spans the rear deck, providing a subtle separation between the fairway and the owners' pool and spa. The outdoor sitting area links to the leisure room through retreating-glass doors.

STUDY — Lancet arches signal a Venetian influence in a room designed for contemplation. Views to the front property maintain a connection with the colonial architecture of the plan.

VERANDA — Open to the leisure room and deck, the veranda features a sheltered outdoor eating area. Massive columns provide definition for the *plein air* retreat, and permit scenery and sunlight to infuse the space. To the left, a fireplace with a carved mahogany-and-stone surround anchors a plush sitting area.

MASTER BEDROOM — Sculpted arches add depth and dimension to the master bedroom, and a peninsular fireplace borders a sitting area framed by views of the side and rear properties. Sliding-glass doors open the master bedroom to the veranda and views of the coastal preserve.

MASTER BATH — Dramatic stained glass divides the floating bathtub from a hidden steam room.

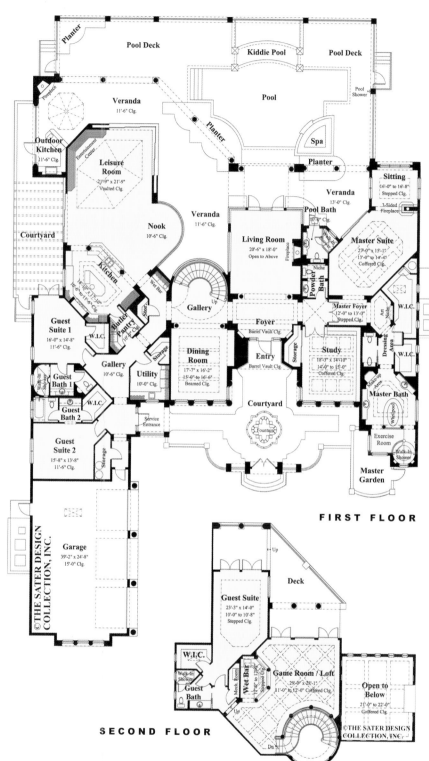

FIRST FLOOR

SECOND FLOOR

©THE SATER DESIGN COLLECTION, INC.

TO ORDER CALL: 1-866-525-9374		PLAN#: DHDS01-6935		*Casa Bellisima*		

TOTAL LIVING	FIRST FLOOR	SECOND FLOOR	BED	BATH	WIDTH	DEPTH	FOUNDATION	PRICE CODE
6524 sq. ft.	5391 sq. ft.	1133 sq. ft.	4	5-1/2	104'0"	140'0"	Slab	0

Home photographed may differ from construction documents.
©The Sater Design Collection, Inc.

© THE SATER DESIGN COLLECTION, INC.

PLAN# DHDS01-6910   **1-866-525-9374**

Seamless transitions from tailored rooms designed for grand events, to comfortable spaces where a shoes-off attitude prevails, reveal the mastery of the design. Past the foyer, the formal dining and living rooms are defined by columns and enjoy generous views of nature. Sculpted ceiling treatments provide a subtle separation between rooms.

In the kitchen, a serving counter overlooks the breakfast area and leisure room. The fireplace provides warmth and character to the common living area, mingled with the atmosphere of the outdoors. Retreating walls extend to the loggia, where an outdoor kitchen handles meals alfresco.

Double doors to the right of the plan lead to the private master wing. On the upper level, a spacious loft overlooks the living room and opens to a deck shared with a guest suite.

STAIRCASE — Carved-wood beams and a vintage medallion soar above the vaulted spaces of the entry hall, emphasizing the dramatic scheme of the home. Just below the foyer level, the wine cellar lends depth and dimension to the gallery, and links spatially to the opposing wet bar.

KITCHEN — The perfect combination of style and function — the kitchen enjoys ample space for a professional grade range and hood, double sinks and spacious dual pantries. Decorative columns accent the eating bar that connects to the leisure room and nook.

REAR VIEW — Views into the casual living area from the rear property reveal an inviting and well-lived-in home, with easy transitions between rooms. Retreating-glass walls bring in a sense of nature to the leisure room and extend its boundaries to the outdoors.

LIVING ROOM — A rotunda ceiling defines the circular dimensions of the heart of the home. The space is surrounded by alcoves, and columns define passage to the formal dining room. A trio of transom windows lends an ecclesiastical layer to a refined scheme that is repeated throughout the home, even in the private retreats.

LEISURE ROOM — Despite its spacious 600 square feet, the leisure room is still one of the coziest rooms in the home, featuring a corner fireplace, built-in entertainment center, exposed-beam ceiling and zero-corner sliding glass doors that open onto the loggia.

STUDY — Rich accents in wood bring an aura of Old-World grace and sophistication to a private study adjacent to the formal living room.

BREAKFAST NOOK — Wide mitered windows share the outdoors, and visually extend the casual living spaces to the loggia. Outdoor sitting and eating areas provide shelter from the sun.

MASTER BEDROOM — The master suite is truly a haven, replete with morning kitchen and his-and-her walk-in closets. One of the crown jewels in this opulent design, the sitting area opens to the loggia via French doors. For pure enjoyment, simply add an evening cocktail or morning coffee.

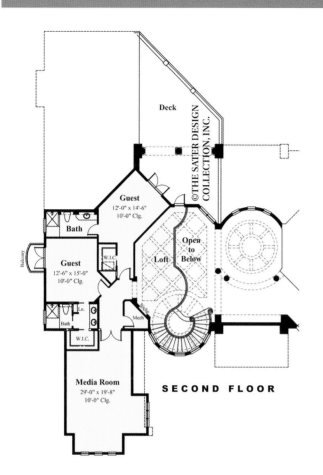

SECOND FLOOR

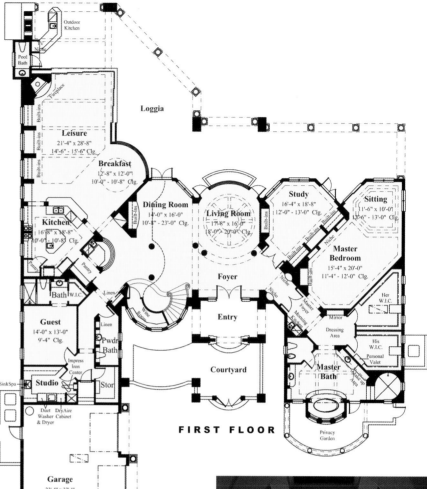

FIRST FLOOR

©THE SATER DESIGN COLLECTION, INC.

LOFT — The loft above the dining area — its boundaries defined by an ornate, wrought-iron railing — provides access to two spacious, second-story guest suites and an observation deck.

MASTER BATH — Crema Marfil marble tile surrounds the step-up tub in the owners' private bath. A trio of windows permits glimpses of a privacy garden surrounding the bay.

TO ORDER CALL: 1-866-525-9374		PLAN#: DHDS01-6910			*Fiorentino*			
TOTAL LIVING	**FIRST FLOOR**	**SECOND FLOOR**	**BED**	**BATH**	**WIDTH**	**DEPTH**	**FOUNDATION**	**PRICE CODE**
6273 sq. ft.	4742 sq. ft.	1531 sq. ft.	4	4F/2H	96'0"	134'8"	Slab	0

Home photographed may differ from construction documents.

Sterling Oaks

©THE SATER DESIGN COLLECTION, INC.

PLAN# DHDS01-6914   **1-866-525-9374**

The wide-hipped roof, classic columns and sweeping arches of the front façade proudly announce this stately estate. Under the porte-cochere, family and friends are embraced by a dramatic entry and led into the grand interior, where stylish columns and arches are repeated throughout.

Rooms flow seamlessly from one to another, and offer generous views of the outdoors. Bedrooms are cozily sequestered into private spaces, each with a full bath area. The master wing is a true haven with a grand bedroom, two walk-in closets and a spa-like bath. Two adjoining gallery areas, each with unique ceiling treatments, serve to divide the wing from the rest of the home.

The second floor offers limitless entertaining and living possibilities with a multi-purpose loft, two complete guests suites and two outdoor decks.

DINING ROOM — The dining room epitomizes stylish elegance with fluid arches — a graceful arched ceiling, built-in buffet with arching mirror and dramatic window. Situated between the kitchen and living room, this exotic space offers the ideal ambience for elegant dining.

KITCHEN — Entertaining is once again the theme in this spacious kitchen, which boasts generous portions of everything from food preparation and pantry space to built-in appliances and breakfast bar seating. The ornamental hood and cabinet moldings add a Tuscan flair.

LIVING ROOM — Tuscan columns delineate the boundaries of the spectacular living room. A stunning view of this gracious entertainment area is enjoyed from the second-story loft and highlights one of the living room's main attractions — a stone fireplace boasting an ornate stone mantle and two-story chimney.

VERANDAH — A second-story balcony bounded by wrought-iron balustrades extends from the rear elevation. Two stories of curved glass meet at the water's edge to create an elegant focal point on the verandah.

LIVING ROOM — The living room's soaring curved and coffered ceiling, as grand as it is, serves merely as the stage for the star performer — a spectacular twenty-two-foot, bowed-glass wall.

REAR VIEW — As viewed from the master suite, the rear elevation is well lighted and inviting. Around every corner a window, archway or balcony welcomes the outside in.

LOFT — At the top of a staircase tucked at the front of the home, the second floor offers limitless entertaining and living possibilities with a multi-purpose loft perfect for game tables and media components.

NOOK/KITCHEN — Central to the heart of the home is the leisure/kitchen/nook. All nestled under stepped ceilings, this core for family gatherings and grand entertaining flows effortlessly together and offers connection to the verandah via mitered-glass windows and disappearing-glass walls.

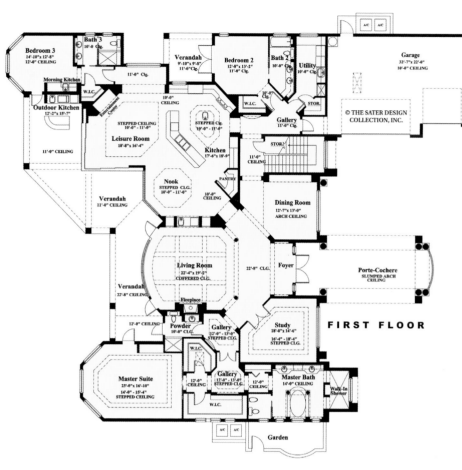

FIRST FLOOR

MASTER BATH — Encased in marble, the master tub views a serene, private garden through tall column-accented windows.

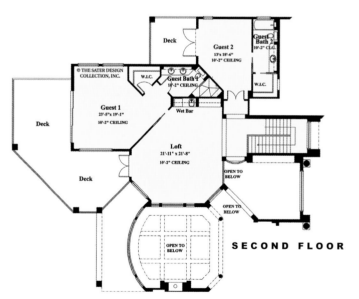

SECOND FLOOR

PORTE-COCHERE — A grand porte-cochere offers more than just shelter from the elements; it offers an imperial welcome to guests.

TO ORDER CALL: 1-866-525-9374	PLAN#: DHDS01-6914	*Sterling Oaks*

TOTAL LIVING	FIRST FLOOR	SECOND FLOOR	BED	BATH	WIDTH	DEPTH	FOUNDATION	PRICE CODE
5816 sq. ft.	4385 sq. ft.	1431 sq. ft.	5	5-1/2	88'0"	110'1"	Slab	0

Home photographed may differ from construction documents.

©The Sater Design Collection, Inc.

© 1997 FRANK BETZ ASSOCIATES, INC.

PLAN# DHFB01-1025   1-866-525-9374

A truly remarkable design, the *Westmoreland* was designed for the home-owner who's looking for upscale living with a casual and comfortable feel. A classic brick exterior is hugged by a cozy wraparound porch. Its breath-taking two-story foyer leads you to the gallery with a curved staircase that makes a lasting impression. A fireplace, built-in cabinetry and bookshelves, create a dramatic focal wall in the two-story family room. A bedroom on the main floor makes a comfortable place for guests, or can be used as a study. The master suite steps up to a tranquil sitting room with its own fireplace giving homeowners a peaceful place to retreat to at the end of the day.

Photographed home and its materials may differ from construction documents.

FOYER — The foyer presents a grand entrance to the home, the overlook on the second floor draws the eyes to the dramatic two-story ceilings.

DINING ROOM — Wainscoting and rich colors provide a comfortable backdrop for this formal dining room.

FAMILY ROOM — French doors and two stories of windows highlight the family room, while built-in shelves and custom molding add elegant flair.

KITCHEN/NOOK — The warm colors of the cabinetry and floors compliment the stainless-steel appliances, creating an inviting area for meal preparation.

LIVING ROOM — The rich colors promote a sense of tranquility and grace.

MASTER BEDROOM — The arched entrance to the sitting room creates a calming effect in the master suite.

MASTER BATH — A radius window flanked by two plant shelves illuminates the master bath, while a privy and double vanities provide convenience and privacy.

GUEST BEDROOM — The guest room on the main level is the perfect place for elderly guests or those who desire privacy.

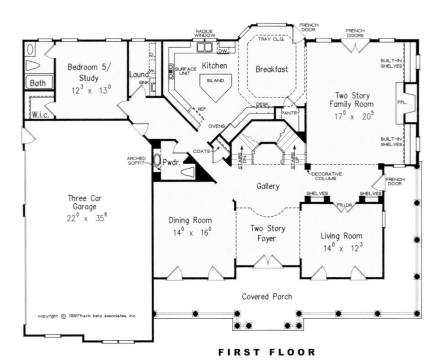

FIRST FLOOR

GALLERY VIEW — The foyer opens up to the gallery which boasts built-in shelves that flank the living room.

REAR ELEVATION

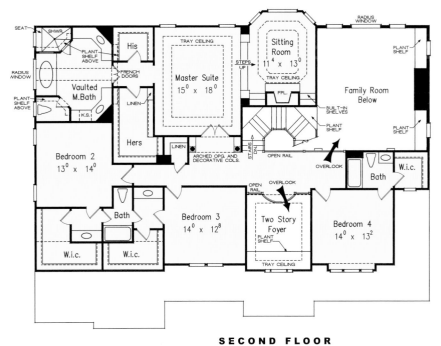

SECOND FLOOR

TO ORDER CALL: 1-866-525-9374	PLAN#: DHFB01-1025	*Westmoreland*

TOTAL LIVING	FIRST FLOOR	SECOND FLOOR	BED	BATH	WIDTH	DEPTH	FOUNDATION	PRICE CODE
4135 sq. ft.	2037 sq. ft.	2098 sq. ft.	5	4-1/2	68'6"	53'0"	Basement, Crawl Space or Slab	J

Home photographed may differ from construction documents.

©1997 Frank Betz Associates, Inc.

WWW.DESIGNER-DREAMHOMES.COM | **39**

© 1994 FRANK BETZ ASSOCIATES, INC.

PLAN# DHFB01-792 | 1-866-525-9374

This expansive home is perfect for entertaining or for large families. A spacious, amenity-filled kitchen gives way to a vaulted family room complete with its own covered porch. A convenient butler's pantry enhances the formal dining room, while the breakfast room is perfect for a more casual dining atmosphere. An impressive two-story library sits at the front of the home, and is accented by a cozy fireplace. The master suite is truly spectacular, with decorative columns, a double vanity in the bathroom, and separate shower and garden tub. Upstairs, there are three additional bedrooms and a rear covered porch.

NOOK — The breakfast nook is framed by a brick knee wall.

MASTER BEDROOM — Columns, arches and a coffered ceiling create a luxurious suite.

DINING ROOM — The dining room is crowned with a domed ceiling and a wall of windows allowing in the natural light.

FAMILY ROOM — French doors and a radius window allow access and views to the backyard.

KITCHEN — Plenty of counter and cabinet space make this kitchen an entertainer's dream.

REAR ELEVATION

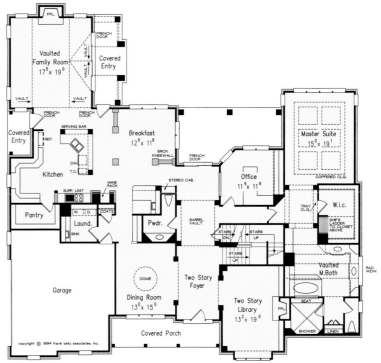

FIRST FLOOR

SECOND FLOOR

	TO ORDER CALL: 1-866-525-9374		PLAN#: DHFB01-792		*Hermitage*				

TOTAL LIVING	FIRST FLOOR	SECOND FLOOR	OPT. BONUS	BED	BATH	WIDTH	DEPTH	FOUNDATION	PRICE CODE
4458 sq. ft.	3218 sq. ft.	1240 sq. ft.	656 sq. ft.	4	3-1/2	76'0"	73'10"	Basement or Crawl Space	J

Home photographed may differ from construction documents.

© 2000 DONALD A. GARDNER, INC.

PLAN# **DHDG01-868**   **1-866-525-9374**

This home's commanding brick exterior with arch-topped windows, quoins, covered entry and hip roof creates a stunning presence, while its spacious interior is equally impressive.

An exciting second-floor balcony overlooks the vaulted foyer and great room. Two sets of French doors flank the great room's fireplace and lead to the back porch and patio. Note the built-in shelves and clerestory dormer windows in the great room. The adjacent kitchen is generously proportioned, featuring a sizable work island and nearby built-in desk and walk-in pantry.

A short hall provides extra privacy for the first-floor master suite, which enjoys a tray ceiling, fireplace, back-porch access, his-and-her walk-in closets and bath with garden tub.

The three-car garage includes additional space for storage.

GREAT ROOM — The vaulted ceiling, twin sets of French doors and stunning fireplace showcase architectural details and luxury in the great room.

KITCHEN — A cookbook library built into the center island keeps recipes handy in this chef's dream of a kitchen.

MASTER BEDROOM — A second fireplace in the master bedroom provides warmth and elegance to the suite.

REAR VIEW — Twin dormers and columns highlight the back porch giving the rear exterior a striking façade.

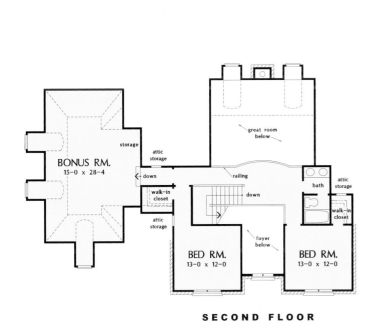

SECOND FLOOR

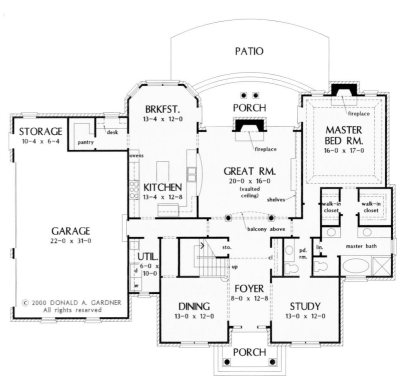

FIRST FLOOR

*Other foundation options available. See page 255

TO ORDER CALL: 1-866-525-9374			PLAN#: DHDG01-868				*Santerini*			
TOTAL LIVING	FIRST FLOOR	SECOND FLOOR	BONUS ROOM	BED	BATH	WIDTH	DEPTH	FOUNDATION		PRICE CODE
2955 sq. ft.	2270 sq. ft.	685 sq. ft.	563 sq. ft.	3	2-1/2	75'1"	53'6"	Crawl Space*		F

Home photographed may differ from construction documents.

Frank Betz Associates
ESTATE COLLECTION

Greythorne

PLAN#:
DHFB01-3764

TO ORDER CALL:
1-866-525-9374

TOTAL LIVING	FIRST FLOOR	SECOND FLOOR	BONUS ROOM	BED	BATH	WIDTH	DEPTH	FOUNDATION	PRICE CODE
2587 sq. ft.	2047 sq. ft.	540 sq. ft.	278 sq. ft.	4	3	60'0"	56'0"	Basement, Crawl Space or Slab	I

©2002 Frank Betz Associates, Inc.

Thoughtful and creative design makes the *Greythorne* unique in both the layout and the details. The full-service kitchen has an attention-grabbing coffered ceiling. Adjoining this room is a vaulted grand room with a fireplace. Accessible from both the master suite and the keeping room is a covered back porch — a quiet place to retreat after a busy day. Window seats are incorporated into the master suite and the fourth bedroom.

REAR ELEVATION

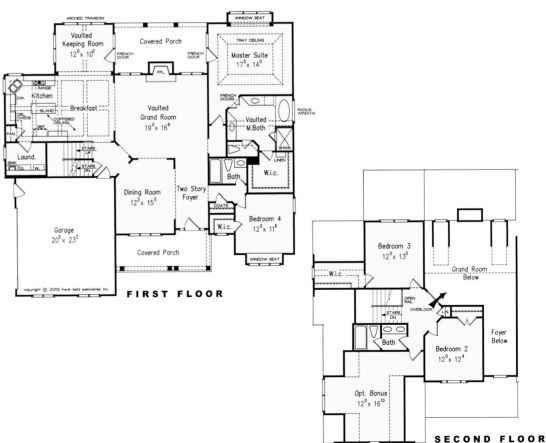

FIRST FLOOR

SECOND FLOOR

44 | **DESIGNER DREAM HOMES**

TO ORDER CALL: 1-866-525-9374	PLAN#: DHDS01-6602					*Turnberry Lane*			
TOTAL LIVING	**FIRST FLOOR**	**SECOND FLOOR**	**BED**	**BATH**	**WIDTH**	**DEPTH**	**FOUNDATION**	**PRICE CODE**	
2794 sq. ft.	2794 sq. ft.	N/A	3	3	70'0"	98'0"	Slab	**H**	

©The Sater Design Collection, Inc.

Home photographed may differ from construction documents.

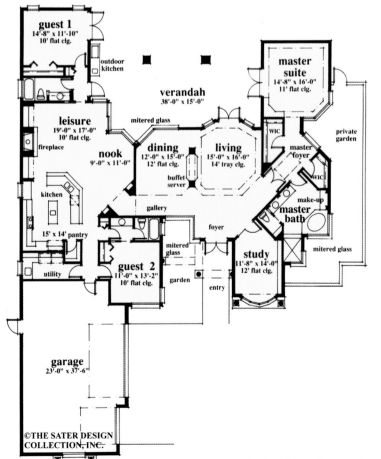

Decorative columns, circle-head windows and a double-arched entryway add curb appeal to this view-oriented design. Inside the foyer, a mitered glass window provides open views. The formal living and dining rooms are straight ahead, with a unique buffet server connecting the rooms. To connect to the outdoors, nearly every room to the rear of the plan opens to the verandah.

REAR VIEW

Westhampton

	PLAN#: DHFB01-3767		TO ORDER CALL: 1-866-525-9374

TOTAL LIVING	FIRST FLOOR	SECOND FLOOR	BED	BATH	WIDTH	DEPTH	FOUNDATION	PRICE CODE
3012 sq. ft.	1974 sq. ft.	1038 sq. ft.	4	3-1/2	72'0"	57'0"	Basement or Crawl Space	I

The distinctive stone exterior of the *Westhampton* sets the stage for the unique layout inside. A cozy keeping room is situated adjacent to the kitchen, creating uncommon angles rarely found in stock home plans. A built-in desk is incorporated to the upper floor, giving children a perfect place to do homework or crafts.

REAR ELEVATION

FIRST FLOOR

SECOND FLOOR

TO ORDER CALL: 1-866-525-9374	PLAN#: DHDG01-1048	*Hartford*

TOTAL LIVING	FIRST FLOOR	SECOND FLOOR	BONUS ROOM	BED	BATH	WIDTH	DEPTH	FOUNDATION	PRICE CODE
3155 sq. ft.	2395 sq. ft.	760 sq. ft.	454 sq. ft.	4	4	63'9"	63'11"	Crawl Space*	G

©2004 Donald A. Gardner, Inc.

*Other foundation options available. See page 255

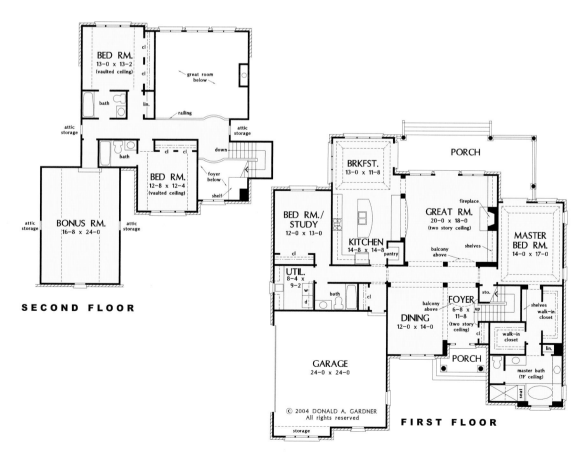

SECOND FLOOR

FIRST FLOOR

Gables create an impression on this towering traditional. A metal roof caps the front porch, and arched transoms add architectural interest. Inside, a curved balcony and columns divide the foyer from the great room. Built-in cabinetry, a walk-in pantry and mudroom closet add convenience. An island and service counter complete the kitchen. Flexible space includes a study/bedroom and bonus room.

REAR ELEVATION

Hickory Ridge

	PLAN#: DHDG01-916	TO ORDER CALL: 1-866-525-9374

TOTAL LIVING	FIRST FLOOR	SECOND FLOOR	BONUS ROOM	BED	BATH	WIDTH	DEPTH	FOUNDATION	PRICE CODE
3167 sq. ft.	2194 sq. ft.	973 sq. ft.	281 sq. ft.	4	3-1/2	71'11"	54'4"	Crawl Space*	G

*Other foundation options available. See page 255

From an abundance of counter space and large walk-in pantry to the built-ins and storage areas, this design makes the most of space. Supported by columns, a curved balcony overlooks the two-story great room. The powder room is easily accessible from the common rooms, and angled corners soften the dining room. An upstairs bedroom is equipped with its own bath.

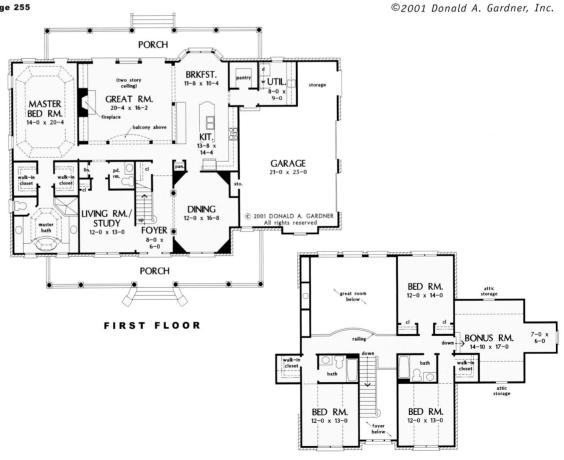

FIRST FLOOR

SECOND FLOOR

REAR ELEVATION

TO ORDER CALL: 1-866-525-9374	PLAN#: DHFB01-3769	*Muirfield*

TOTAL LIVING	FIRST FLOOR	SECOND FLOOR	BED	BATH	WIDTH	DEPTH	FOUNDATION	PRICE CODE
3189 sq. ft.	2153 sq. ft.	1036 sq. ft.	4	3-1/2	72'0"	60'6"	Basement or Crawl Space	I

©2002 Frank Betz Associates, Inc.

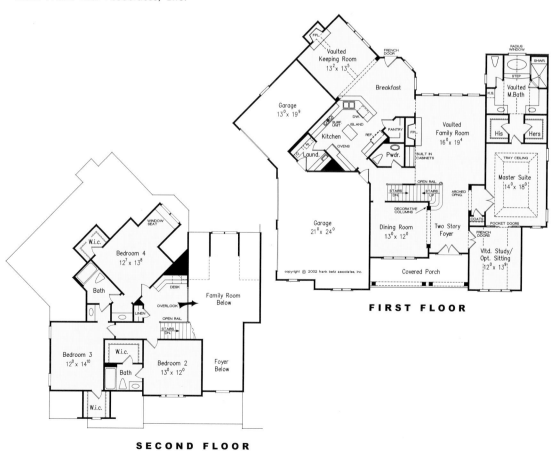

FIRST FLOOR

SECOND FLOOR

The *Muirfield* was designed to cater to the lifestyle of today's growing family. The kitchen, breakfast area and vaulted keeping room create a unified space for casual family time. His-and-her closets and a lavish master bath create a "Suite" spot to start and end your day. A built-in desk in the second-floor loft creates the perfect homework station for kids.

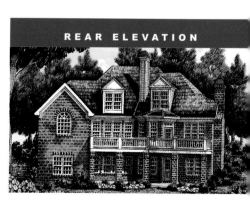

REAR ELEVATION

Wilshire

PLAN#: DHFB01-994						**TO ORDER CALL:** 1-866-525-9374			

TOTAL LIVING	FIRST FLOOR	SECOND FLOOR	BED	BATH	WIDTH	DEPTH	FOUNDATION	PRICE CODE
3215 sq. ft.	1583 sq. ft.	1632 sq. ft.	5	4-1/2	58'4"	50'0"	Basement, Crawl Space or Slab	I

©1996 Frank Betz Associates, Inc.

Multiple gables and a low maintenance exterior give a dramatic finish to this Traditional home. Inside all secondary bedrooms are located on the second floor. The master suite boasts a sitting room with a fireplace. The breakfast room and two-story family room are adjoining making entertaining or family time a breeze. Additionally, a bedroom on the main level can act as such or be converted to a home office.

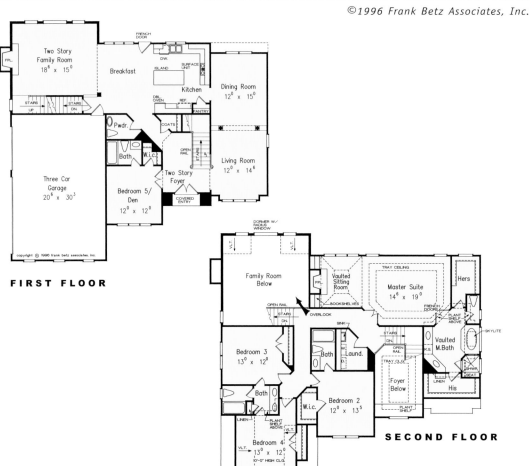

REAR ELEVATION

TO ORDER CALL:	PLAN#:	*Spring Hill Lane*
1-866-525-9374	DHDS01-6661	

TOTAL LIVING	FIRST FLOOR	SECOND FLOOR	BED	BATH	WIDTH	DEPTH	FOUNDATION	PRICE CODE
3301 sq. ft.	3301 sq. ft.	N/A	4	3-1/2	80'0"	103'8"	Slab	H

©The Sater Design Collection, Inc.

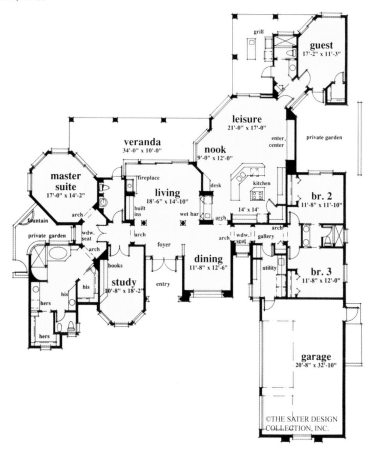

©THE SATER DESIGN COLLECTION, INC.

One-story living at its best, an open-floor plan is combined with a split-bedroom layout to create comfortable living spaces and private retreats. The living room features built-in cabinetry, a fireplace, wet bar and glass doors to the veranda. The kitchen is equipped with a built-in desk, eating bar and large pantry. Arches line the gallery that flows throughout the home.

REAR ELEVATION

Governor's Club Way

PLAN#: DHDS01-6674						**TO ORDER CALL:** 1-866-525-9374		

TOTAL LIVING	FIRST FLOOR	SECOND FLOOR	BED	BATH	WIDTH	DEPTH	FOUNDATION	PRICE CODE
3398 sq. ft.	3398 sq. ft.	N/A	3	3-1/2	121'5"	96'2"	Slab	H

Home photographed may differ from construction documents.

This custom-feel ranch provides an expansive layout that opens up to outdoor views and creates two distinctive wings — one for the private master retreat and another for family living spaces and secondary bedrooms. A veranda wraps the entire rear and provides multiple outdoor living opportunities.

REAR ELEVATION

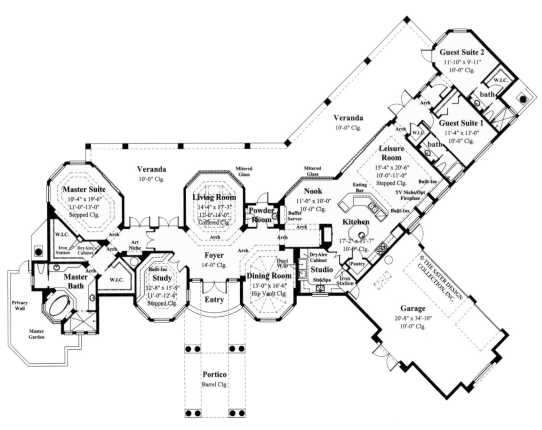

TO ORDER CALL: 1-866-525-9374	PLAN#: DHFB01-3917	*Westborough*

TOTAL LIVING	FIRST FLOOR	SECOND FLOOR	BONUS ROOM	BED	BATH	WIDTH	DEPTH	FOUNDATION	PRICE CODE
3467 sq. ft.	2550 sq. ft.	917 sq. ft.	736 sq. ft.	4	5	63'10"	85'0"	Basement, Crawl Space or Slab	I

©2005 Frank Betz Associates, Inc.

SECOND FLOOR

FIRST FLOOR

The covered porch and courtyard entry welcome you to the *Westborough*. Inside the foyer leads to the vaulted family room that includes a fireplace, built-in cabinets and a rear wall of windows that allows views to the back yard. The master suite encompasses one wing of the home. A loft on the second floor has French doors that open, overlooking the keeping room, adjacent to the kitchen.

REAR ELEVATION

Wellingly

PLAN#: DHDG01-943							**TO ORDER CALL:** 1-866-525-9374			

TOTAL LIVING	FIRST FLOOR	SECOND FLOOR	BONUS ROOM	BED	BATH	WIDTH	DEPTH	FOUNDATION	PRICE CODE
3573 sq. ft.	2511 sq. ft.	1062 sq. ft.	465 sq. ft.	4	3-1/2	84'11"	55'11"	Crawl Space*	H

*Other foundation options available. See page 255

This estate house is full of architectural details. A bay window expands the dining room, while a curved balcony overlooks the two-story great room. Fireplaces, flanked by built-ins, highlight the great room and master bedroom, and a gentle curve extends the breakfast nook. A three-car garage, formal study and versatile bonus room make living comfortable, while decorative ceilings add elegance.

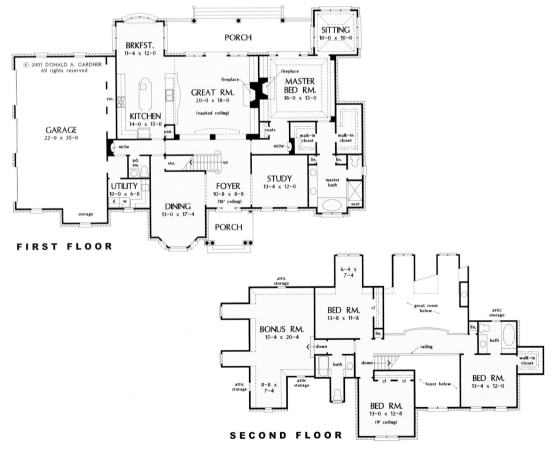

FIRST FLOOR

SECOND FLOOR

REAR ELEVATION

TO ORDER CALL:
1-866-525-9374

PLAN#:
DHFB01-3757

Woodcliffe

TOTAL LIVING	FIRST FLOOR	SECOND FLOOR	BONUS ROOM	BED	BATH	WIDTH	DEPTH	FOUNDATION	PRICE CODE
3585 sq. ft.	2225 sq. ft.	1360 sq. ft.	234 sq. ft.	4	3-1/2	68'10"	60'0"	Basement or Crawl Space	I

©2002 Frank Betz Associates, Inc.

SECOND FLOOR

FIRST FLOOR

Casual elegance describes the *Woodcliffe*, with its timber accented gables and a cupola and weather vane atop the garage. Coffered ceilings create interesting dimension throughout the main level of this home. A large family recreation room is incorporated into the upper level, providing flexible options like a media room or exercise area.

REAR ELEVATION

Cedar Ridge

	PLAN#:	TO ORDER CALL:
	DHDG01-1125-D	1-866-525-9374

TOTAL LIVING	FIRST FLOOR	BASEMENT	BONUS ROOM	BED	BATH	WIDTH	DEPTH	FOUNDATION	PRICE CODE
3678 sq. ft.	2405 sq. ft.	1273 sq. ft.	679 sq. ft.	3	4	62'10"	64'2"	Hillside Walkout	0

As the *2005 Progressive Farmer Idea House*, this gorgeous Craftsman home exposes rich architectural detail throughout the open floor plan. A sunroom, rear deck and screen porch are all on the main level, while the lower level boasts a screen porch with summer kitchen, as well as a second covered porch. Entertaining spaces continue with the lower-level entertainment room with wet bar.

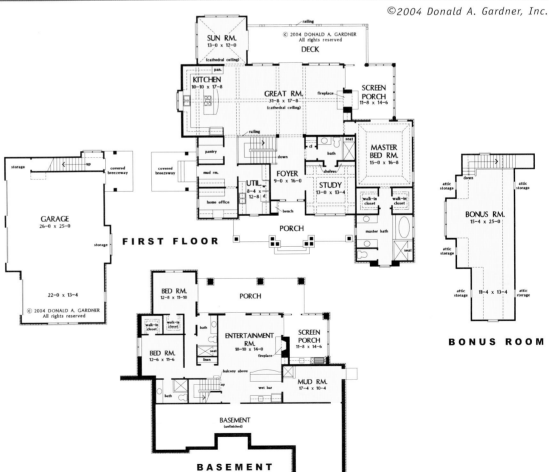

FIRST FLOOR

BONUS ROOM

BASEMENT

REAR ELEVATION

TO ORDER CALL: 1-866-525-9374	PLAN#: DHDS01-6660	*Sunningdale Cove*

TOTAL LIVING	FIRST FLOOR	SECOND FLOOR	GUEST HOUSE	BED	BATH	WIDTH	DEPTH	FOUNDATION	PRICE CODE
3744 sq. ft.	2822 sq. ft.	610 sq. ft.	312 sq. ft.	4	3-1/2	80'0"	96'0"	Slab	J

©The Sater Design Collection, Inc.

Home photographed may differ from construction documents.

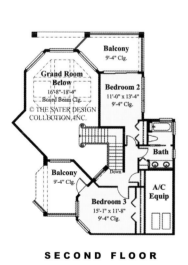

SECOND FLOOR

FIRST FLOOR

This truly unique courtyard plan was designed to bring outdoor living inside. What appears to be a stately entry into the home is, in fact, a portico entry that grants access to a spacious courtyard. The home is wrapped around a central pool area, creating striking views from all the family areas as well as from second-floor observation decks.

REAR VIEW

Fiddler's Creek

PLAN#: DHDS01-6746							**TO ORDER CALL:** 1-866-525-9374		

TOTAL LIVING	FIRST FLOOR	SECOND FLOOR	BED	BATH	WIDTH	DEPTH	FOUNDATION	PRICE CODE
3893 sq. ft.	2841 sq. ft.	1052 sq. ft.	4	3-1/2	85'0"	76'2"	Slab or Opt. Basement	I

©*The Sater Design Collection, Inc.*

With a floor plan that is perfect for any region, custom-feel design elements are the highlight of this stylish home. Past the foyer, the two-story living room features bay-glass windows and a double-sided fireplace shared with the study. A spiral staircase, high ceilings, oversized rooms, built-in cabinetry, art niches and an elegant façade make this home a timeless choice.

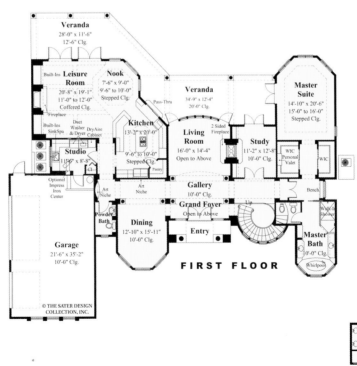

FIRST FLOOR

SECOND FLOOR

REAR ELEVATION

TO ORDER CALL: 1-866-525-9374		PLAN#: DHAL01-5002		*Maple Manor*					
TOTAL LIVING	**FIRST FLOOR**	**BASEMENT**	**BED**	**BATH**	**WIDTH**	**DEPTH**	**FOUNDATION**		**PRICE CODE**
4093 sq. ft.	2665 sq. ft.	1428 sq. ft.	3	3-1/2	106'0"	67'10"	Hillside Walkout		0

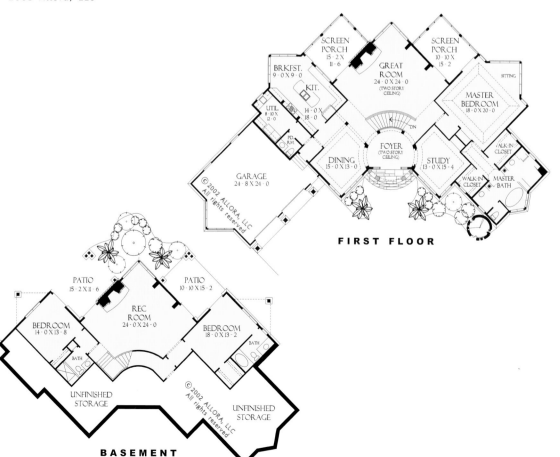

FIRST FLOOR

BASEMENT

A towering stone entrance guides family and friends inside where they're greeted by a two-story foyer. The great room features a tray ceiling, striking fireplace and French doors to dual screened porches. Glasswork extends the breakfast nook and master sitting area, while built-in cabinetry adds elegance. The rec room is flanked by covered porches and highlighted by a second fireplace.

Stoney Creek Way

	PLAN#:	TO ORDER CALL:
	DHDS01-6656	1-866-525-9374

TOTAL LIVING	FIRST FLOOR	SECOND FLOOR	BED	BATH	WIDTH	DEPTH	FOUNDATION	PRICE CODE
4140 sq. ft.	3053 sq. ft.	1087 sq. ft.	4	3-1/2	87'4"	80'4"	Basement	L

Home photographed may differ from construction documents.

©The Sater Design Collection, Inc.

A unique layout, extraordinary detailing and elegant façade make this home a timeless choice for every family. An open layout ensures flow for everyday living, though entertaining on a grand scale is an easy task. The living room features a fireplace, two-story ceiling and bayed glass doors. A gallery hallway leads down each wing of the home and is graced with columns.

REAR ELEVATION

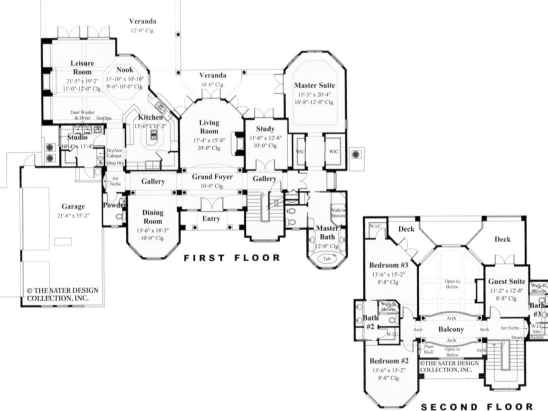

TO ORDER CALL:
1-866-525-9374

PLAN#:
DHDS01-6942

Marrakesh

TOTAL LIVING	FIRST FLOOR	GUEST SUITE	BED	BATH	WIDTH	DEPTH	FOUNDATION	PRICE CODE
5109 sq. ft.	4705 sq. ft.	404 sq. ft.	4	4-1/2	100'0"	138'10"	Slab	0

©The Sater Design Collection, Inc.

Home photographed may differ from construction documents.

This villa displays an affinity for the outdoors, with large expanses of glass that absorb the scenery. An open arrangement of the living and dining rooms creates an entertainment area completed by a wine cellar. Retreating-glass doors connect the casual living zone and the outdoor spaces, which includes an alfresco kitchen and a solana with a fireplace.

REAR VIEW

REAR VIEW

Heatherstone

	PLAN#: DHAL01-5016		TO ORDER CALL: 1-866-525-9374

TOTAL LIVING	FIRST FLOOR	BASEMENT	BONUS ROOM	BED	BATH	WIDTH	DEPTH	FOUNDATION	PRICE CODE
6155 sq. ft.	4088 sq. ft.	2067 sq. ft.	523 sq. ft.	4	4F/2H	119'2"	100'7"	Hillside Walkout	0

A stone exterior and multiple gables give this home a distinguished façade. Inside, this 6000+ square foot home is nothing short of luxury. Coffered ceilings crown the library and dining room. The generous master suite overflows with detail and space, and be sure to note the screen porch with outdoor fireplace.

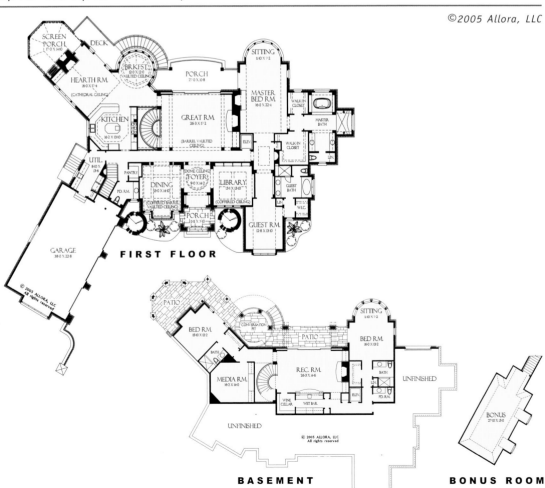

FIRST FLOOR

BASEMENT

BONUS ROOM

REAR ELEVATION

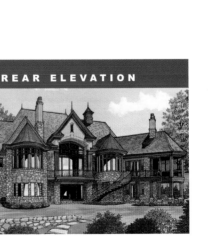

TO ORDER CALL: 1-866-525-9374	PLAN#: DHCS01-M6300A2S2FD-0	*Windermere*

TOTAL LIVING	FIRST FLOOR	SECOND FLOOR	BED	BATH	WIDTH	DEPTH	FOUNDATION	PRICE CODE
6300 sq. ft.	2895 sq. ft.	3405 sq. ft.	4	5-1/2	124'4"	70'10"	Crawl Space	N

©CornerStone Designs, LLC

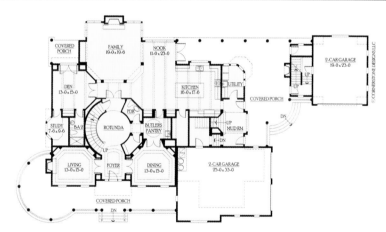

FIRST FLOOR

A spectacular farmhouse loaded with luxury, the *Windermere* brings a new level of elegance to a favorite traditional style. Family-friendly features abound, from the circular-covered entry porch and dramatic stair rotunda, to the grand family areas and expansive loggia linking to the detached garage and mother-in-law studio. The master and children's suites are truly exceptional.

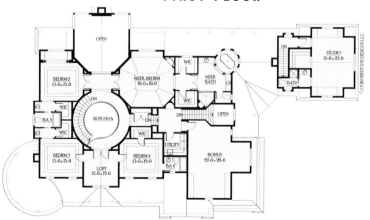

SECOND FLOOR

REAR ELEVATION

Hemingway

	PLAN#:	TO ORDER CALL:
	DHGA01-05224	1-866-525-9374

TOTAL LIVING	FIRST FLOOR	SECOND FLOOR	OPT. BASEMENT	BED	BATH	WIDTH	DEPTH	FOUNDATION	PRICE CODE
6354 sq. ft.	3754 sq. ft.	2600 sq. ft.	3497 sq. ft.	6	6F/3H	83'7"	96'10"	Basement	0

Home photographed may differ from construction documents.

©*Garrell Associates, Inc.*

A warm welcome feeling is created by this American Stick-Style architecture which features a stone-and-shake exterior. The spacious first-floor plan includes a large covered porch with a fireplace, sun room and deck — inviting hours of entertaining for family and friends. Also on the main floor is an elegant master suite providing privacy and relaxation with a special feature of a two-story closet. The second floor boasts four-bedroom suites.

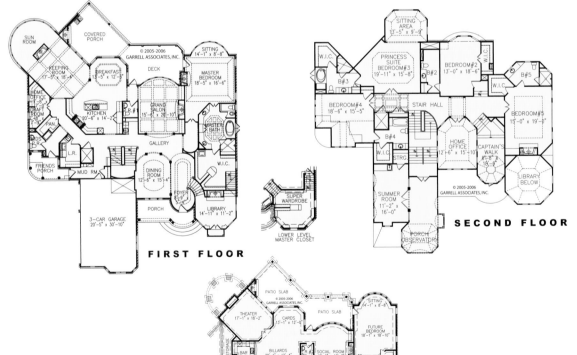

FIRST FLOOR

SECOND FLOOR

OPT. BASEMENT

REAR VIEW

TO ORDER CALL: 1-866-525-9374	PLAN#: DHCS01-M7400A4S-0	*Shenandoah*

TOTAL LIVING	FIRST FLOOR	SECOND FLOOR	BED	BATH	WIDTH	DEPTH	FOUNDATION	PRICE CODE
7400 sq. ft.	3970 sq. ft.	3430 sq. ft.	5	5-1/2	136'0"	125'6"	Crawl Space	0

©CornerStone Designs, LLC

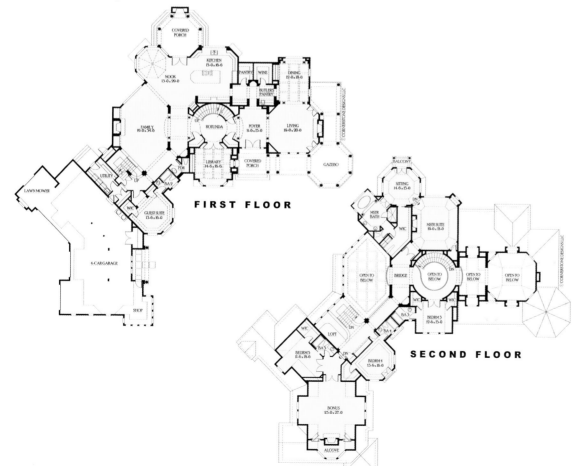

FIRST FLOOR

SECOND FLOOR

A shingle-style mansion on a grand scale, this American classic is full of luxury and charm. Its sweeping façades are highlighted by sculptural columned porches, gazebos, bays, turrets, and dormers. Carefully designed alignments and interior volumes create dramatic spatial sequences throughout the home. Packed with thoughtful features, the *Shenandoah* is a perfect balance of elegance, coziness and style.

REAR ELEVATION

European Collection

Cedar Court -
DONALD A. GARDNER ARCHITECTS -
See page 68

Cedar Court - KITCHEN

Balance Old-World elegance with modern sensibilities,

and you create home plans with a strong sense of grace, excitement,

history and beauty. Witness the elegant porticos and charming, romantic balconies,

combined with the lovely, multiple rooflines that provide such a strong feeling of

another time and place. And the stately beauty flows

throughout the substantial grand rooms; through the wide-open, distinctive foyers

and up the sweeping, grand staircases. Lofts, bedrooms, guest suites and master

retreats all extend themselves and flow further, out to verandas and lanais.

These and many more stunning European touches combine in these plans to provide

ample opportunities to entertain, relax and live in style.

Avalon Manor -
GARRELL ASSOCIATES - See page 94

© 2003 ALLORA, LLC

PLAN#   DHAL01-5004   1-866-525-9374

Stone and stucco combine to add a touch of European elegance to the *Cedar Court*. A towering stone wall — topped with a gable — creates the perfect frame for an impressive front entry, while arched windows and vents soften this hillside walkout's strong exterior. Perfect for lakeside lots or those who want to capitalize on the seclusion of the mountains, the *Cedar Court* is true luxury.

Outdoor living is accommodated in grand style. With a decorative chimney cap, a massive fireplace highlights the screened-turret porch, extending outdoor enjoyment time. The wrapping rear porch, along with the basement-level patio, provides an abundance of recreation space.

DINING ROOM — Wooden columns punctuate the entrance to the dining room, while chocolate-colored molding frames the room.

GREAT ROOM — Exposed wooden beams and a serving bar connect the great room to the kitchen for a truly open feel.

KITCHEN — Tile and granite contrast with furniture-style cabinetry, and a large center island features a gas range and additional storage.

SITTING AREA — The master bedroom features a bayed sitting area that is framed by a wall of windows to usher natural light throughout the room.

GREAT ROOM — Highlighting the great room, this colossal fireplace creates a grand focal point, while windows, transoms and French doors invite views inside.

MASTER BEDROOM — A tray ceiling and towering windows add to the spaciousness of the master bedroom.

REAR VIEW — Porches, patios, striking gable peaks and French doors combine to create a rear exterior that is truly stunning.

MASTER BATH — Intricate tile work, a double vanity and open shower create a unique master bath.

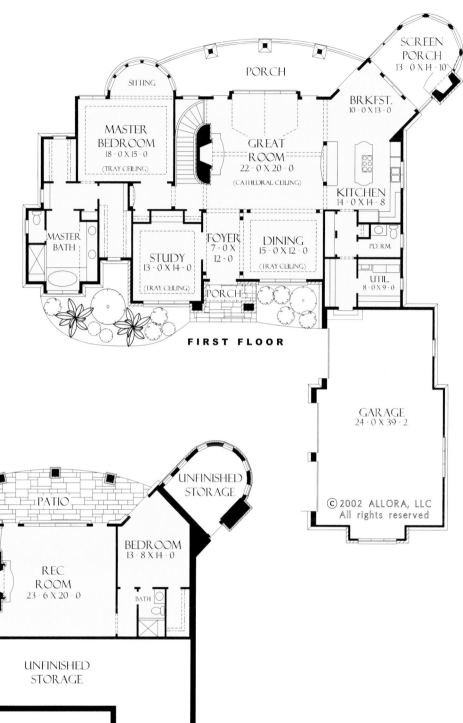

FIRST FLOOR

BASEMENT

TO ORDER CALL: 1-866-525-9374	PLAN#: DHAL01-5004	*Cedar Court*

TOTAL LIVING	FIRST FLOOR	BASEMENT	BED	BATH	WIDTH	DEPTH	FOUNDATION	PRICE CODE
3820 sq. ft.	2446 sq. ft.	1374 sq. ft.	3	3-1/2	82'4"	95'10"	Hillside Walk-out	0

Home photographed may differ from construction documents.

Lansdowne Place

© GARRELL ASSOCIATES, INC.

PLAN# DHGA01-01068   1-866-525-9374

From a two-story living room and foyer, to multiple fireplaces and an entertainment room, the *Lansdowne Place* boasts lavish architectural detail throughout. For the homeowner that appreciates privacy and an abundance of living spaces, this home has it all!

The loftiness of the exterior is echoed throughout the interior as well. A grand two-story foyer welcomes guests, while the two-story living room becomes the ideal entertaining area. Architectural detail is evidenced by a large laundry room, rear staircase, intimate porches, a gallery and library complete with a fireplace. The master suite is nothing short of grandiose. It features an expansive walk-in closet, master bath, and is complete with a separate sitting area and morning kitchen.

The second-floor bedrooms are conveniently spread apart from one another and feature their own private bathrooms. An optional bonus room is located above the garage and is designed with enough room for just about any type of entertainment, making this floor plan not only versatile but practical.

STAIRCASE — This sweeping staircase creates a grand entrance for entertaining and welcoming guests into the home. It sets the stage for the entire home with its awe inspiring entry into the two-story vaulted foyer.

KITCHEN — The uniquely angled serving island in the kitchen provides space for four people as well as additional preparation area for the chef of the family.

LIVING ROOM — This magnificent two-story living room features a bow-window view as well as a fireplace framed by cabinetry. This room is ideal for entertaining and providing a picturesque view into the rear gardens. The rear staircase located between the living room and breakfast area leads to the upstairs gallery that takes in spectacular views.

LIBRARY — Located off the foyer, the spacious library or music room opens to the master suite through French doors. It boasts a triple-arched window and cozy fireplace just waiting for its residents to relax and enjoy the room.

FAMILY ROOM — An open, yet warm family room angles off the kitchen to create abundant space for family and friends to gather. This room is punctuated by a fireplace, vaulted ceiling and wall of windows.

MASTER BEDROOM — A luxurious private retreat is created by this first-floor master suite. The ultimate hideaway for relaxation can be found in a separate sitting area with a morning kitchen as well as a tucked away master bath. An expansive walk-in closet completes this perfect master suite.

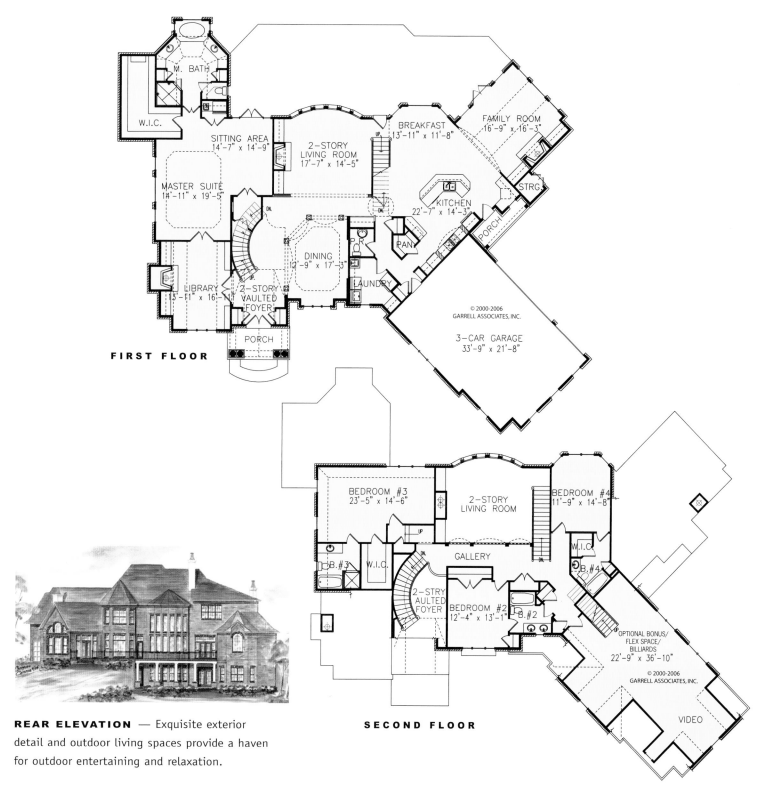

FIRST FLOOR

© 2000-2006 GARRELL ASSOCIATES, INC.

SECOND FLOOR

REAR ELEVATION — Exquisite exterior detail and outdoor living spaces provide a haven for outdoor entertaining and relaxation.

TO ORDER CALL: 1-866-525-9374	PLAN#: DHGA01-01068	*Lansdowne Place*

TOTAL LIVING	FIRST FLOOR	SECOND FLOOR	BONUS ROOM	BED	BATH	WIDTH	DEPTH	FOUNDATION	PRICE CODE
4376 sq. ft.	3061 sq. ft.	1315 sq. ft.	679 sq. ft.	4	4-1/2	95'5"	80'2"	Basement or Crawl Space	0

Home photographed may differ from construction documents.

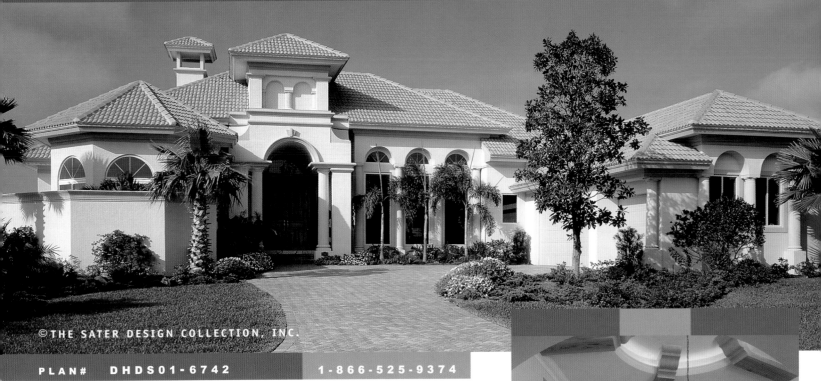

© THE SATER DESIGN COLLECTION, INC.

PLAN# DHDS01-6742   1-866-525-9374

This stylish design combines inviting outdoor living spaces with an impressive, open floor plan. Pilasters line an arcade of windows that repeat the sculpted form of the entry. The open foyer enjoys views past the living room through two sets of French doors and a wall of glass. A graceful colonnade borders the formal dining room.

Conveniently located near the dining room, state-of-the-art amenities prepare the kitchen for any occasion. With commercial-grade appliances and enough food-preparation space for two cooks, the kitchen easily serves the connected breakfast nook and leisure room. An angled hearth in the leisure room creates a comfortable atmosphere that flows all the way to the breakfast nook. The entire wing opens through retreating doors to the side courtyard, which includes an outdoor fireplace.

DINING ROOM — Square columns and repeating arches define the formal dining room. Transom windows, dual art niches and a high domed ceiling — trimmed in cypress wood — combine to create an elegant atmosphere.

KITCHEN — Ample counter space, double ovens and a large walk-in pantry make this kitchen a chef's dream. The recessed window with window seat overlooks a courtyard with a stone fireplace. A convenient eating bar connects the kitchen to the leisure room.

FORMAL LIVING ROOM — The living room, with access to the lanai via two sets of French doors, is set apart from the dining and foyer area by Tuscan columns and made even more unique by an octagonal ceiling with inlaid wood. Attention to detail is evident throughout, from carved coffers to majestic marble flooring.

LEISURE ROOM — An angled entertainment center, wet bar and nearby kitchen combine to create the welcoming atmosphere of the leisure room. A stair hall connects the casual living space with secluded guest quarters and leads to a single glass door, which provides access to an outdoor kitchen. The entire wing opens through retreating doors to the side courtyard, which includes an outdoor fireplace.

GUEST SUITE — Children of all ages will enjoy the playful guest retreat at "Camp Grandma." Sliding-glass doors offer outdoor fun, while the nearby kitchen offers the possibility of a midnight snack.

MASTER BATH — Topped with decorative corbels, an ornately carved partition wall separates the Roman tub from a spacious walk-in shower designed for two. Arch-top windows supply ample panoramas of the master garden.

MASTER BEDROOM — A private groin-vaulted foyer leads into the master retreat. Sitting under a step-up tray ceiling, the master retreat features sliding-glass doors to the lanai, a cozy bay window sitting area, luxurious bath and spacious walk-in closets.

REAR VIEW — The ideal place for an informal meal or drinks, the spacious lanai features an outdoor grill and is conveniently accessible from the master suite, formal living and leisure rooms.

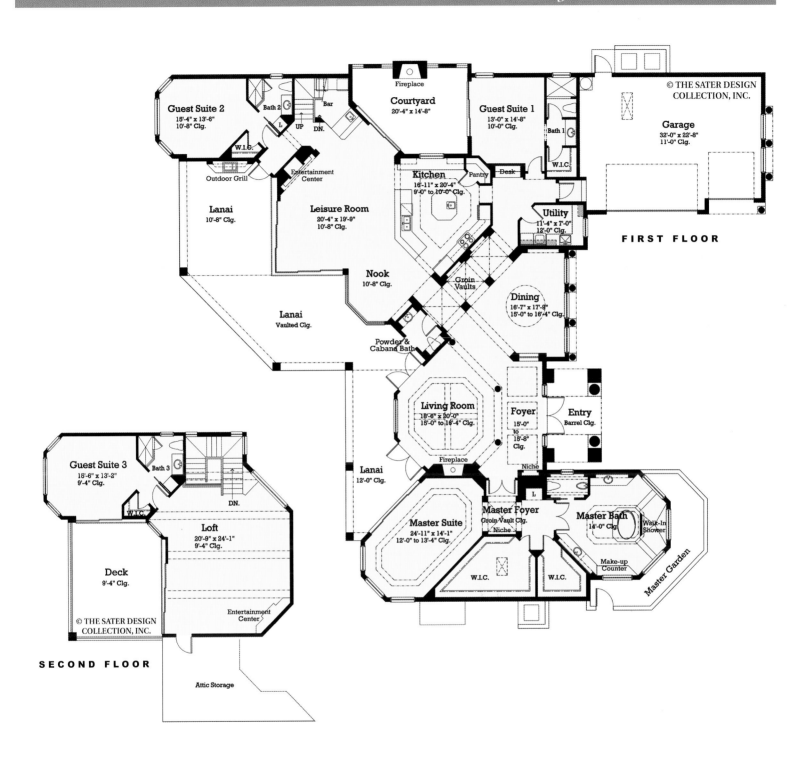

FIRST FLOOR

© THE SATER DESIGN COLLECTION, INC.

SECOND FLOOR

Not available for construction in Lee and Collier Counties, Florida

TO ORDER CALL: 1-866-525-9374	**PLAN#:** DHDS01-6742	*Sherbrooke*				

TOTAL LIVING	FIRST FLOOR	SECOND FLOOR	BED	BATH	WIDTH	DEPTH	FOUNDATION	PRICE CODE
4771 sq. ft.	3933 sq. ft.	838 sq. ft.	4	4-1/2	91'4"	109'0"	Slab	0

Home photographed may differ from construction documents.

©The Sater Design Collection, Inc.

Summerfield

© 2000 FRANK BETZ ASSOCIATES, INC.

PLAN# DHFB01-3550   1-866-525-9374

The stone front porch with columns and multiple rooflines give this home the appearance of a storybook cottage. A vaulted keeping room with a fireplace also boasts radius windows along the rear of the home, allowing views to the backyard. Additionally, the openness of the floor plan allows for easy access from the family room to the kitchen and into the keeping room. This makes entertaining especially easy. The main-level master suite has a large sitting area that is flanked by decorative columns; meanwhile the master bath boasts his-and-her closets and a separate tub and shower. Two secondary bedrooms and an optional bonus room, reside on the second floor.

FOYER — The two-story foyer features transoms that frame the front door and an overhead Palladian window for added illumination.

DEN — Modified from the original plan, these homeowners chose to add an additional room on the second floor to create more room for family interaction.

GREAT ROOM — The great room features a centrally located fireplace and vibrant wall color to create the ultimate entertaining space.

DINING ROOM — Triple windows allow natural light to flow into the dining room. Together with the hardwood floors, this creates a warm and inviting space.

REAR VIEW

STUDY — Deviating from the original plan, this study creates a convenient and useful space for a home office.

MASTER BEDROOM — A tray ceiling tops the master bedroom, showcasing architectural detail, while the vaulted sitting area increases the room's depth.

KITCHEN — The serving bar creates extra seating in the kitchen, while black appliances nicely complement the hardwood floors and cabinetry.

FIRST FLOOR

Vaulted M.Bath · Vaulted Great Room 15⁶ x 20² · Breakfast · Vaulted Keeping Room 13⁰ x 17⁰ · Kitchen · Hers · His · Master Suite 14⁰ x 16³ · Two Story Foyer · Dining Room 12⁰ x 13⁰ · Garage 21⁵ x 24⁶ · Pwdr. · Pantry · Laund. · Sitting Area 14⁰ x 10⁰ · Covered Porch

copyright © 2000 frank betz associates, inc.

MASTER BATH — Truly relaxing, the master bath features a radius window and vaulted ceiling that draw the eye upwards in a luxurious fashion.

KEEPING ROOM — The vaulted keeping room includes a second fireplace and built-in shelves and cabinetry for showcasing knick-knacks and family photos.

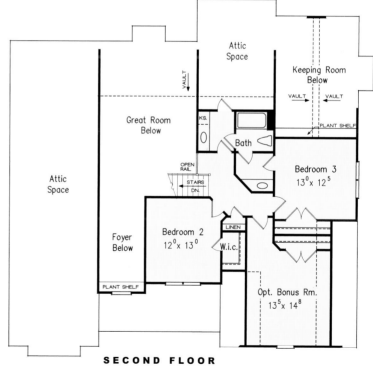

SECOND FLOOR

Attic Space · Great Room Below · Keeping Room Below · Bath · Bedroom 3 13⁰ x 12⁵ · Foyer Below · Bedroom 2 12⁰ x 13⁰ · W.i.c. · Opt. Bonus Rm. 13⁵ x 14⁸

TO ORDER CALL: 1-866-525-9374	PLAN#: DHFB01-3550	*Summerfield*	

TOTAL LIVING	FIRST FLOOR	SECOND FLOOR	BONUS ROOM	BED	BATH	WIDTH	DEPTH	FOUNDATION	PRICE CODE
2680 sq. ft.	2087 sq. ft.	593 sq. ft.	249 sq. ft.	3	2-1/2	58'4"	55'2"	Basement or Crawl Space	G

Home photographed may differ from construction documents.

Mallory

PLAN# DHFB01-992   **1-866-525-9374**

Brick and siding accents give the *Mallory* a casual elegance that Old-World style encompasses. Inside, thoughtful consideration was given to this smart and functional floor plan. Everyone knows that family members and guests tend to congregate in the kitchen. The *Mallory* accommodates this fact, with a vaulted breakfast area and keeping room with fireplace adjoining the kitchen. The master suite is conveniently located on the main level, giving the homeowners a private retreat. Two secondary bedrooms — each with a walk-in closet — share a divided bathing area on the second floor. An optional bonus room is ready to finish into a fourth bedroom, playroom or exercise area.

Photographed home and its materials may differ from construction documents.

KEEPING ROOM — Accessible directly from the kitchen, this keeping room's an ideal spot for entertaining.

KITCHEN — The open kitchen overlooks both a vaulted breakfast room and keeping room.

GREAT ROOM — Custom molding around the fireplace adds an elegant look to the vaulted great room.

DINING ROOM — Chair rail molding grants style to the dining room, while easy access to the kitchen provides convenience.

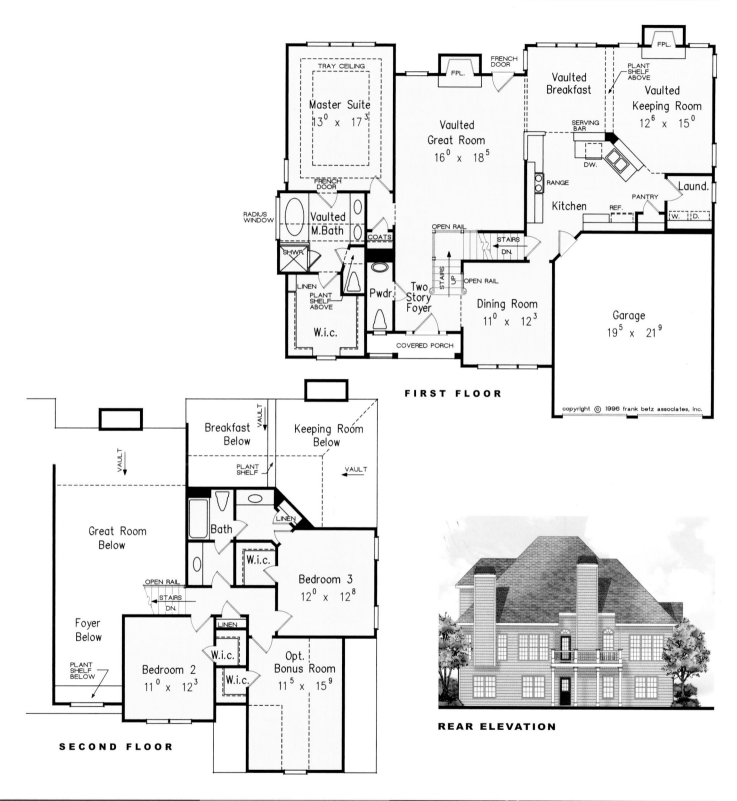

FIRST FLOOR

copyright © 1996 frank betz associates, inc.

SECOND FLOOR

REAR ELEVATION

TO ORDER CALL: 1-866-525-9374	PLAN#: DHFB01-992	*Mallory*

TOTAL LIVING	FIRST FLOOR	SECOND FLOOR	BONUS ROOM	BED	BATH	WIDTH	DEPTH	FOUNDATION	PRICE CODE
2155 sq. ft.	1628 sq. ft.	527 sq. ft.	207 sq. ft.	3	2-1/2	54'0"	46'10"	Basement, Crawl Space or Slab	I

Home photographed may differ from construction documents.

© GARRELL ASSOCIATES, INC.

PLAN# DHGA01-01250   **1-866-525-9374**

This European classic boasts a wonderful series of front gables, which give the impression that this two-story beauty is bursting with lots of space... a perception that is truly accurate. With its five bedrooms, one an extravagant master suite, or the two-story grand room, a sense of stunning spaciousness reigns. The master suite provides a private retreat with a fireplace, over-size master bath, and his-and-her walk-in closets. On the first floor, both a library and a home office can be found, along with an expansive gallery hallway and a gracious dining room. For sheer working space and convenience the island kitchen is extraordinary. It opens easily to a keeping room and large breakfast area, which leads to an inviting rear deck perfect for outdoor enjoyment.

REAR VIEW — Featuring a large deck, as well as a covered patio, this home is perfect for entertaining.

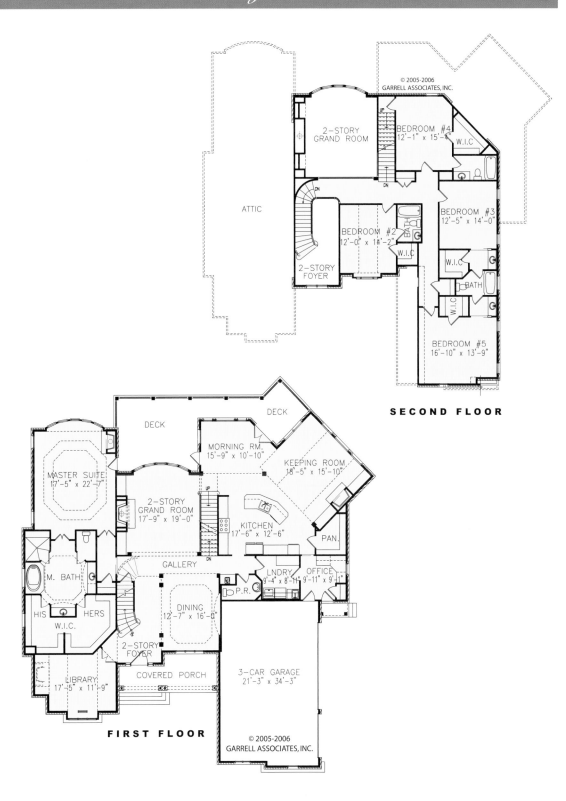

© 2005-2006
GARRELL ASSOCIATES, INC.

ATTIC

2-STORY GRAND ROOM

BEDROOM #4
12'-1" x 15'-4"

W.I.C

BEDROOM #2
12'-0" x 14'-2"

BEDROOM #3
12'-5" x 14'-0"

W.I.C

2-STORY FOYER

BATH

W.I.C

W.I.C

BATH

W.I.C

BEDROOM #5
16'-10" x 13'-9"

SECOND FLOOR

DECK

DECK

MORNING RM.
15'-9" x 10'-10"

KEEPING ROOM
18'-5" x 15'-10"

MASTER SUITE
17'-5" x 22'-7"

2-STORY GRAND ROOM
17'-9" x 19'-0"

KITCHEN
17'-6" x 12'-6"

PAN.

M. BATH

GALLERY

LNDRY
9'-4" x 8'-11"

OFFICE
9'-11" x 9'-1"

HIS   HERS

W.I.C.

DINING
12'-7" x 16'-0"

P.R.

2-STORY FOYER

LIBRARY
17'-5" x 11'-9"

COVERED PORCH

3-CAR GARAGE
21'-3" x 34'-3"

FIRST FLOOR

© 2005-2006
GARRELL ASSOCIATES, INC.

TO ORDER CALL: 1-866-525-9374	PLAN#: DHGA01-01250	*Belle Demure Lorraine*

TOTAL LIVING	FIRST FLOOR	SECOND FLOOR	BED	BATH	WIDTH	DEPTH	FOUNDATION	PRICE CODE
4478 sq. ft.	3072 sq. ft.	1406 sq. ft.	5	4-1/2	75'5"	73'11"	Basement	0

Home photographed may differ from construction documents.

© THE SATER DESIGN COLLECTION, INC.

PLAN# DHDS01-6756   **1-866-525-9374**

Warm and intimate, this design offers well thought out family living spaces, elegant and functional interior details, a Mediterranean façade and portico entry. Multiple connections with the outdoors provide opportunities for gatherings large and small.

The interior is filled with architectural details intended to provide easy living amidst elegant appointments. In the kitchen an angled counter, center island and sophisticated appliances please the most discerning cook. Adjacent is an eating nook and leisure room with access to the lanai. A built-in entertainment center, dry bar and a server niche guarantee easy entertaining.

The dining and formal living rooms offer an opulent setting for entertaining. A deep coffer embraces fine art and furniture in the dining room while built-in bookshelves add a special touch to the living room.

LIVING ROOM — Fresh breezes through corner pocket disappearing-glass doors infuse the formal living room with a serene, alfresco ambience.

KITCHEN — An angled counter, center island and sophisticated appliances please the most discerning cook.

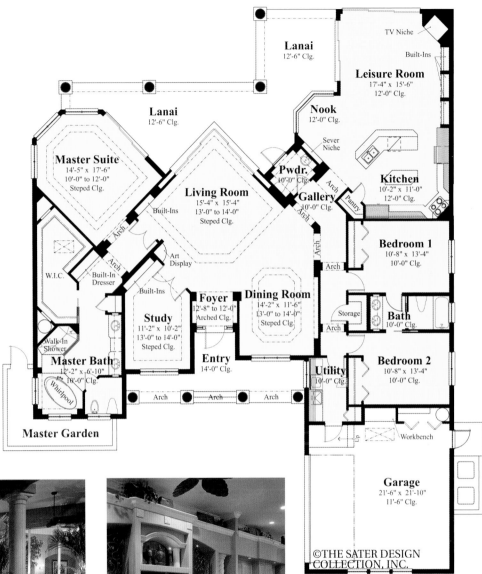

Lanai
12'-6" Clg.

TV Niche

Built-Ins

Leisure Room
17'-4" x 15'-6"
12'-0" Clg.

Lanai
12'-6" Clg.

Nook
12'-0" Clg.

Sever Niche

Kitchen
10'-2" x 11'-0"
12'-0" Clg.

Master Suite
14'-5" x 17'-6"
10'-0" to 12'-0"
Steped Clg.

Pwdr.
10'-0" Clg.

Gallery
10'-0" Clg.

Living Room
15'-4" x 15'-4"
13'-0" to 14'-0"
Steped Clg.

Built-Ins

Pantry

Arch

Arch

Bedroom 1
10'-8" x 13'-4"
10'-0" Clg.

W.I.C.

Arch

Built-In Dresser

Art Display

Built-Ins

Arch

Storage

Bath
10'-0" Clg.

Study
11'-2" x 10'-2"
13'-0" to 14'-0"
Steped Clg.

Foyer
12'-8" to 12'-0"
Arched Clg.

Dining Room
14'-2" x 11'-6"
13'-0" to 14'-0"
Steped Clg.

Arch

Walk-In Shower

Entry
14'-0" Clg.

Bedroom 2
10'-8" x 13'-4"
10'-0" Clg.

Utility
10'-0" Clg.

Master Bath
12'-2" x 6'-10"
10'-0" Clg.

Whirlpool

Arch

Arch

Arch

Workbench

Master Garden

Garage
21'-6" x 21'-10"
11'-6" Clg.

©THE SATER DESIGN COLLECTION, INC.

NOOK — Adjacent to the kitchen, the windowed eating nook enjoys a connection with the outdoors as well as the leisure room.

REAR VIEW — The winding, covered lanai embraces the home's rear rooms and free flowing pool, while offering cozy sitting and dining areas for every occasion.

LEISURE ROOM — A built-in entertainment center, dry bar and a server niche creates a natural gathering spot with easy kitchen access.

TO ORDER CALL: 1-866-525-9374		PLAN#: DHDS01-6756		*Kinsey*					
TOTAL LIVING	**FIRST FLOOR**	**SECOND FLOOR**	**BED**	**BATH**	**WIDTH**	**DEPTH**	**FOUNDATION**		**PRICE CODE**
2907 sq. ft.	2907 sq. ft.	N/A	3	2-1/2	65'0"	84'0"	Slab		G

Home photographed may differ from construction documents.

Summerlyn

© 2002 FRANK BETZ ASSOCIATES, INC.

PLAN#   DHFB01-3675   1-866-525-9374

A t a glance it's clear to see that the *Summerlyn* is an all-around unique and extraordinary design. A warm blend of brick and cedar shake with stone accents grace the exterior of the home. An attention-grabbing two-story turret is perhaps the most unique feature of the façade. More pleasant surprises await you inside. A sunken sunroom off the breakfast area shares a see-thru fireplace with the family room. Here, a bowed wall of windows allows the light to stream in, making this a bright and sunny room. Upstairs, the master bath features decorative niches on each end of the tub, allowing the homeowner to add personal decorating touches. The master suite also includes a spacious sitting room.

FAMILY ROOM — A raised hearth of fieldstone is the perfect resting place next to a roaring fire. A bowed wall of floor-to-ceiling windows floods this room with daylight.

KITCHEN — With its antique pine flooring and bead-board ceiling, this eating area has a warm cozy feel.

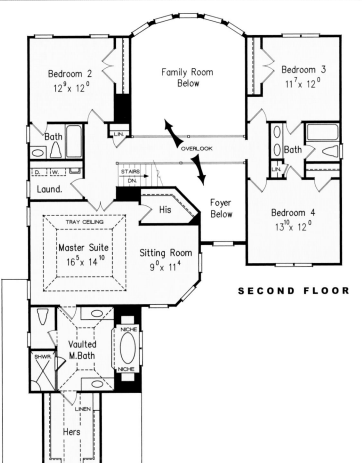

SECOND FLOOR

MASTER BEDROOM — A sitting room with built-in cabinets, turret and fireplace is the perfect place to begin and end the day.

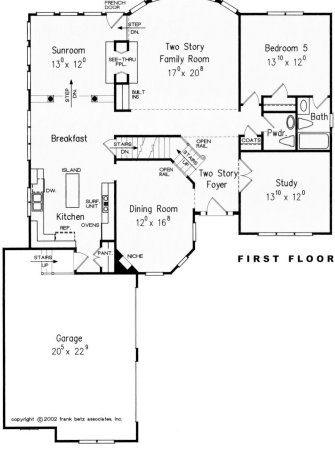

FIRST FLOOR

REAR VIEW

TO ORDER CALL: 1-866-525-9374	PLAN#: DHFB01-3675	*Summerlyn*

TOTAL LIVING	FIRST FLOOR	SECOND FLOOR	BED	BATH	WIDTH	DEPTH	FOUNDATION	PRICE CODE
3281 sq. ft.	1685 sq. ft.	1596 sq. ft.	5	4-1/2	51'0"	66'10"	Basement, Crawl Space or Slab	I

Home photographed may differ from construction documents.

PLAN# DHGA01-05319   **1-866-525-9374**

This Normandy country home brings together timeless architecture and an open flowing floor plan. Its angled garage offers an interesting flair to the exterior view. The porch welcomes you into the magnificent two-story vaulted foyer with a sweeping staircase. The main-level formal rooms share an open space that boasts a glorious bow window with exquisite views. The kitchen, breakfast and family rooms come together to form an inviting entertainment area for family and friends with access to the outdoor living area. The second floor is complete with a rear staircase, three bedroom suites, as well as a spacious optional bonus area suitable for a game room or home theatre.

REAR VIEW — Featured is a spacious deck, perfect for family and friend gatherings or enjoying a serene setting of rear vistas.

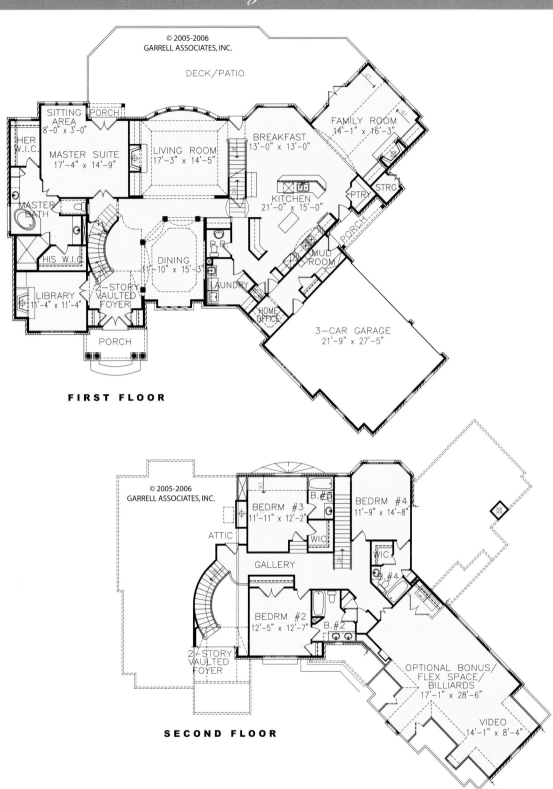

FIRST FLOOR

SECOND FLOOR

TO ORDER CALL: 1-866-525-9374		PLAN#: DHGA01-05319			*Avalon Manor*				
TOTAL LIVING	FIRST FLOOR	SECOND FLOOR	BONUS ROOM	BED	BATH	WIDTH	DEPTH	FOUNDATION	PRICE CODE
3944 sq. ft.	2875 sq. ft.	1069 sq. ft.	685 sq. ft.	4	4-1/2	87'5"	71'9"	Basement or Crawl Space	0

Home photographed may differ from construction documents.

© THE SATER DESIGN COLLECTION, INC.

PLAN#   DHDS01-6651   **1-866-525-9374**

This gracious home offers the perfect blend of public and private spaces, with careful attention dedicated to style and comfort. From the street, the triple-arched entryway warmly welcomes one into the home. An arched gallery leads past the formal dining and living rooms to the family areas. The expansive kitchen easily serves the dining room and nook. As with the living room, the leisure room has three pairs of French doors that open to the veranda.

Down the gallery, toward the opposite wing are the owner's areas. A study can be used for a home office or an exercise room. Double doors lead into the private suite and bath areas. Up the grand staircase, the balcony overlooks the living room and foyer below. Three guest bedrooms, two of which access private balconies, complete the upper level.

LIVING ROOM — Past the columns and arches of the grand foyer, a soaring two-story ceiling, three sets of French doors and transom windows lend to the spaciousness of the formal living room. As cozy as it is grand, the room features built-in cabinetry — perfect for displaying treasured books and pictures — and an inviting fireplace.

NOOK/KITCHEN — The expansive kitchen easily serves the dining room and informal nook. It boasts ample workspace, a walk-in pantry, cooktop island, a wraparound eating bar and a pass-thru to the veranda.

LEISURE ROOM — The substantial leisure room features three sets of glass doors to the veranda, a built-in entertainment center and open access to the kitchen and breakfast nook.

REAR VIEW — Arches and columns line the sizeable veranda, providing a covered retreat from the sun. Accessible from formal and private rooms, the outdoor living space serves as the perfect setting for get togethers large and small.

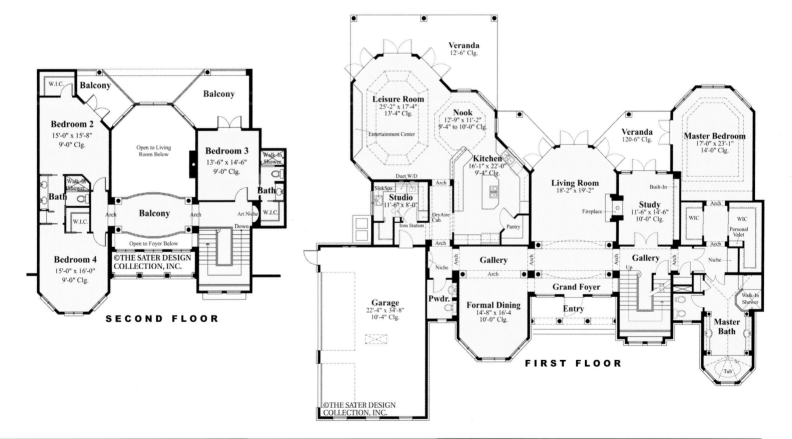

SECOND FLOOR

FIRST FLOOR

©THE SATER DESIGN COLLECTION, INC.

TO ORDER CALL: 1-866-525-9374	PLAN#: DHDS01-6651	*Hillcrest Ridge*

TOTAL LIVING	FIRST FLOOR	SECOND FLOOR	BED	BATH	WIDTH	DEPTH	FOUNDATION	PRICE CODE
4759 sq. ft.	3546 sq. ft.	1213 sq. ft.	4	3-1/2	95'4"	83'0"	Basement	L

Home photographed may differ from construction documents.

Northampton

PLAN# DHFB01-1005   1-866-525-9374

Innovative design details are apparent throughout the *Northampton*. Its façade features a turret and a terrace area, giving it phenomenal curb appeal. The dining room is defined by architectural columns, keeping this space open and accessible to the rest of the main floor. The turreted room makes a beautiful study, but can be easily altered to make a stunning sitting area for the master bedroom. The kitchen overlooks a vaulted keeping room. Its fireplace makes it a cozy place to end the day. Optional bonus space is available on the second floor, allowing the homeowners to finish it as they wish.

KITCHEN — This bright kitchen features elegant cabinetry and a convenient central island with a breakfast bar for quick meals and conversation.

FAMILY ROOM — Columns, a second-floor balcony and a high ceiling keep this family room open to the other gathering rooms.

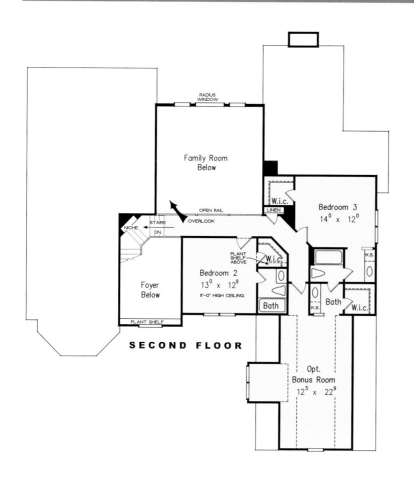

SECOND FLOOR

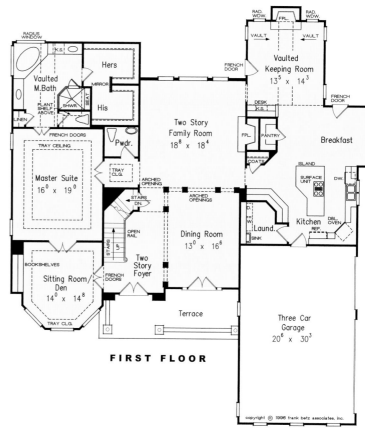

FIRST FLOOR

copyright © 1996 frank betz associates, inc.

FRONT ELEVATION

REAR ELEVATION

TO ORDER CALL: 1-866-525-9374	PLAN#: DHFB01-1005	*Northampton*

TOTAL LIVING	FIRST FLOOR	SECOND FLOOR	BONUS ROOM	BED	BATH	WIDTH	DEPTH	FOUNDATION	PRICE CODE
3083 sq. ft.	2429 sq. ft.	654 sq. ft.	420 sq. ft.	3	3-1/2	63'6"	71'4"	Basement, Crawl Space or Slab	I

Home photographed may differ from construction documents.

Ravencroft

PLAN#:	TO ORDER CALL:
DHDG01-1062	1-866-525-9374

TOTAL LIVING	FIRST FLOOR	BONUS ROOM	BED	BATH	WIDTH	DEPTH	FOUNDATION	PRICE CODE
1821 sq. ft.	1821 sq. ft.	345 sq. ft.	3	2	54'4"	61'4"	Crawl Space*	D

*Other foundation options available. See page 255

A hipped roof combines with stucco and stone to create an elegant elevation with Old-World flair. By using columns and a minimum of walls to designate rooms, the floor plan is remarkably open. Tray ceilings in the formal dining room and private master bedroom, along with cathedral ceilings in the great room and secondary bedroom, add sophistication and visual space.

REAR ELEVATION

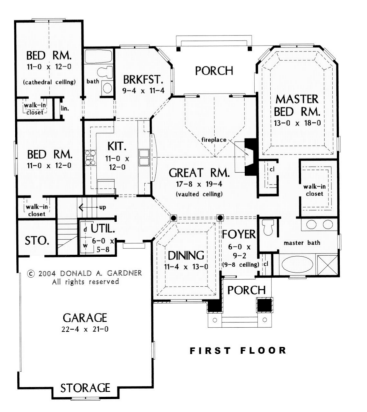

FIRST FLOOR

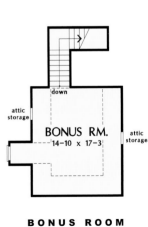

BONUS ROOM

TO ORDER CALL: 1-866-525-9374	PLAN#: DHDS01-8028	*Mercato*

TOTAL LIVING	FIRST FLOOR	SECOND FLOOR	BED	BATH	WIDTH	DEPTH	FOUNDATION	PRICE CODE
2191 sq. ft.	2191 sq. ft.	N/A	3	2-1/2	62'10"	73'6"	Slab or Opt. Basement	F

©*The Sater Design Collection, Inc.*

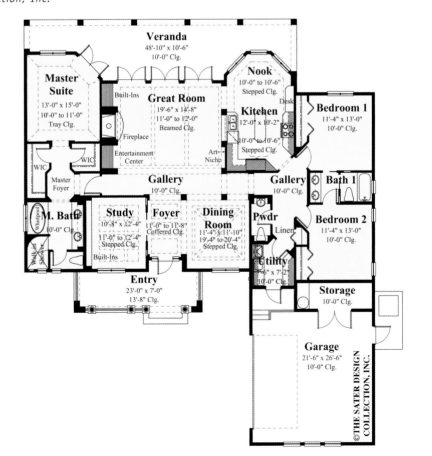

Inside this Mediterranean villa, a beamed ceiling contributes a sense of spaciousness to the home, while walls of glass draw the outdoors in. Varied ceiling treatments and sculpted arches define the wide-open interior, permitting flexibility and views. The great room is anchored by a fireplace flanked by built-in shelves and an entertainment center — visible from the kitchen via a pass-thru.

REAR ELEVATION

Wicklow

	PLAN#:	TO ORDER CALL:
	DHDG01-950	1-866-525-9374

TOTAL LIVING	FIRST FLOOR	SECOND FLOOR	BONUS ROOM	BED	BATH	WIDTH	DEPTH	FOUNDATION	PRICE CODE
2294 sq. ft.	1542 sq. ft.	752 sq. ft.	370 sq. ft.	3	2-1/2	44'4"	54'0"	Crawl Space*	E

*Other foundation options available. See page 255

©2001 Donald A. Gardner, Inc.

A unique mixture of stone, siding and windows create character in this Arts and Crafts design. Columns, decorative railing and a metal roof add architectural interest to an intimate porch. An elegant, curved staircase highlights the grand two-story foyer and great room. The clerestory window floods both the great room and second-floor loft with light.

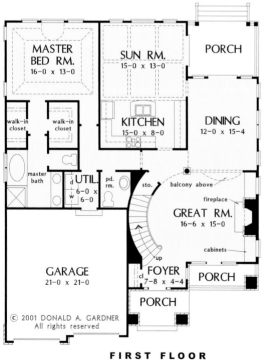

FIRST FLOOR

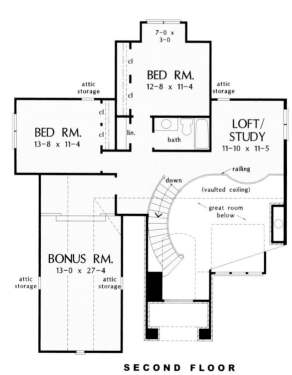

SECOND FLOOR

REAR ELEVATION

TO ORDER CALL: **1-866-525-9374**		**PLAN#:** **DHFB01-969**					*Cassidy*		

TOTAL LIVING	FIRST FLOOR	OPT. SECOND FLOOR	BED	BATH	WIDTH	DEPTH	FOUNDATION	PRICE CODE
2311 sq. ft.	2311 sq. ft.	425 sq. ft.	4	3-1/2	61'0"	65'4"	Basement, Crawl Space or Slab	H

©1996 Frank Betz Associates, Inc.

FIRST FLOOR

OPT. SECOND FLOOR

A smart and functional split-bedroom design, the *Cassidy* is made extra special in its details. The master suite has a private sitting area with a fireplace that gives owners a peaceful place to spend time reading or relaxing. A vaulted ceiling keeps the breakfast room feeling open and bright. Plant shelves and arched openings add touches of character throughout the home.

REAR ELEVATION

Frank Betz Associates
EUROPEAN COLLECTION

Hedgerow	PLAN#: DHFB01-3945	TO ORDER CALL: 1-866-525-9374

TOTAL LIVING	FIRST FLOOR	SECOND FLOOR	BONUS ROOM	BED	BATH	WIDTH	DEPTH	FOUNDATION	PRICE CODE
2324 sq. ft.	1769 sq. ft.	555 sq. ft.	287 sq. ft.	3	2-1/2	59'0"	52'0"	Basement, Crawl Space or Slab	H

©2005 Frank Betz Associates, Inc.

From the front porch to the main-level master suite the *Hedgerow* offers many luxuries that much larger homes provide. The laundry room offers a side entrance with a built-in bench and hooks, providing the ideal place for shoes, coats and book bags. This main-level master floor plan offers a sitting room with built-in bookshelves. A covered entry off of the laundry room allows children and guests to enter and leave their belongings on a built-in bench.

REAR ELEVATION

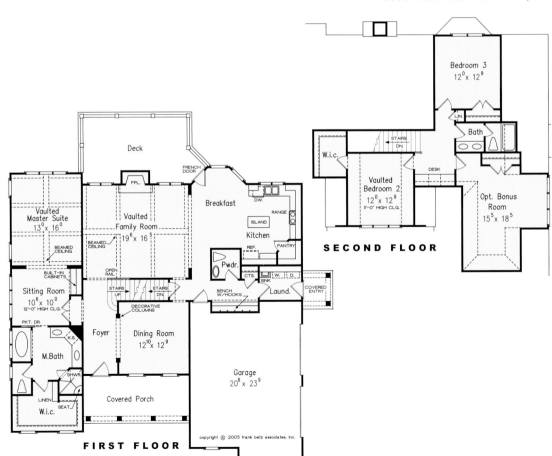

TO ORDER CALL: 1-866-525-9374	PLAN#: DHGA01-06110	*Harmony Mountain Cottage*

TOTAL LIVING	FIRST FLOOR	OPT. KEEPING ROOM	BED	BATH	WIDTH	DEPTH	FOUNDATION	PRICE CODE
2343 sq. ft.	2343 sq. ft.	204 sq. ft.	3	2-1/2	89'11"	70'11"	Slab	0

©Garrell Associates, Inc.

Home photographed may differ from construction documents.

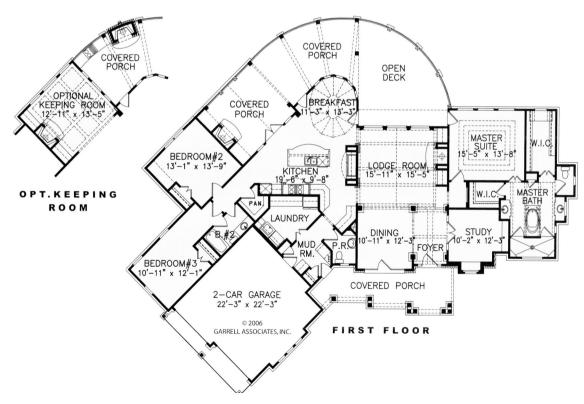

OPT. KEEPING ROOM

FIRST FLOOR

© 2006
GARRELL ASSOCIATES, INC.

Inviting outdoor areas lead to open living spaces with calming views. This ranch home gives the best of all worlds with one-level convenience and ample room both indoors and out for entertaining. The spacious master suite offers a luxurious master bath and double walk-in closets.

Additional versions available: the Tranquility, Amicalola Cottage and Lakeview Cottage (larger).

REAR ELEVATION

Bellavita

PLAN#:
DHDG01-1104

TO ORDER CALL:
1-866-525-9374

TOTAL LIVING	FIRST FLOOR	SECOND FLOOR	BED	BATH	WIDTH	DEPTH	FOUNDATION	PRICE CODE
2369 sq. ft.	2369 sq. ft.	N/A	3	2-1/2	56'0"	70'4"	Crawl Space*	E

*Other foundation options available. See page 255

©2005 Donald A. Gardner, Inc.

Understanding how ceiling treatments can add both vertical volume and architectural detail, this home was designed to impress. Cathedral and tray ceilings top almost every room from the great and breakfast rooms, to the master and secondary bedrooms. Also noteworthy are the built-in shelves and fireplace in both the great room and screened porch.

REAR ELEVATION

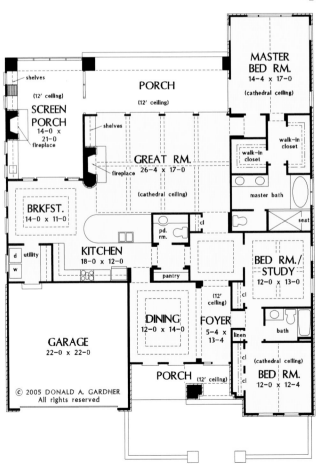

Donald A. Gardner ARCHITECTS

EUROPEAN COLLECTION

PLAN#:
DHDG01-816

Hyde Park

TOTAL LIVING	FIRST FLOOR	SECOND FLOOR	BONUS ROOM	BED	BATH	WIDTH	DEPTH	FOUNDATION	PRICE CODE
2387 sq. ft.	1918 sq. ft.	469 sq. ft.	374 sq. ft.	4	3	73'3"	43'6"	Crawl Space*	E

*Other foundation options available. See page 255

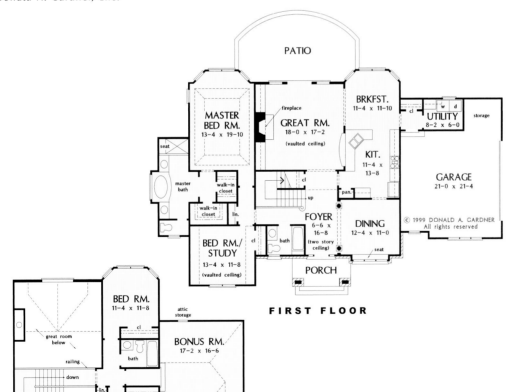

PATIO

MASTER BED RM.
13-4 x 19-10

seat

master bath

walk-in closet

walk-in closet

lin.

cl

bath

BED RM./ STUDY
13-4 x 11-8
(vaulted ceiling)

fireplace

GREAT RM.
18-0 x 17-2
(vaulted ceiling)

cl

up

KIT.
11-4 x 13-8

pan.

FOYER
6-6 x 16-8
(two story ceiling)

PORCH

BRKFST.
11-4 x 11-10

cl

w   d

UTILITY
8-2 x 6-0

storage

GARAGE
21-0 x 21-4

DINING
12-4 x 11-0

seat

© 1999 DONALD A. GARDNER
All rights reserved

FIRST FLOOR

BED RM.
11-4 x 11-8

attic storage

great room below

railing

down

lin.

cl

foyer below

BONUS RM.
17-2 x 16-6

bath

cl

BED RM.
12-8 x 10-8

attic storage

7-4 x 6-3

SECOND FLOOR

Stone and stucco, front-facing gables and large windows create an eye-catching exterior for this home. A two-story ceiling adds height and drama to the formal foyer, which is illuminated by a clerestory above the front door. A box-bay window with lovely window seat enriches the formal dining room. A balcony overlooks both the great room and foyer.

REAR ELEVATION

McKibbon

	PLAN#:	TO ORDER CALL:
	DHDG01-1119	1-866-525-9374

TOTAL LIVING	FIRST FLOOR	BONUS ROOM	BED	BATH	WIDTH	DEPTH	FOUNDATION	PRICE CODE
2645 sq. ft.	2645 sq. ft.	543 sq. ft.	3	2-1/2	67'4"	65'0"	Crawl Space*	F

*Other foundation options available. See page 255

This stunning exterior exquisitely mirrors the lavish interior of this elegant home. The master suite is nothing short of grandiose as it features a spacious sitting area, private porch, tray ceiling and two walk-in closets. A cathedral ceiling highlights the sunroom and great room, while a tray ceiling adorns the dining room.

REAR ELEVATION

FIRST FLOOR

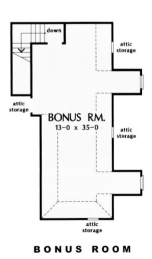

BONUS ROOM

TO ORDER CALL: 1-866-525-9374	PLAN#: DHDG01-1051	*Eton*

TOTAL LIVING	FIRST FLOOR	SECOND FLOOR	BONUS ROOM	BED	BATH	WIDTH	DEPTH	FOUNDATION	PRICE CODE
2717 sq. ft.	2065 sq. ft.	652 sq. ft.	636 sq. ft.	4	4	65'2"	52'8"	Crawl Space*	F

*Other foundation options available. See page 255

FIRST FLOOR

SECOND FLOOR

For those who want a more traditional layout, this floor plan offers distinct room definition. The kitchen island includes a breakfast bar, and a built-in desk provides a place for afternoon homework. Blurring the line between indoor and outdoor living, a screened porch creates a special haven. A large bonus room can be transformed into a home theatre, gym or office.

REAR ELEVATION

Bartolini

	PLAN#:						TO ORDER CALL:	
	DHDS01-8022						1-866-525-9374	

TOTAL LIVING	FIRST FLOOR	SECOND FLOOR	BONUS ROOM	BED	BATH	WIDTH	DEPTH	FOUNDATION	PRICE CODE
2736 sq. ft.	2084 sq. ft.	652 sq. ft.	375 sq. ft.	3	2-1/2	60'6"	94'0"	Slab or Opt. Basement	G

©The Sater Design Collection, Inc.

A graceful entry arcade set off by arches, pilasters and a groin-vaulted ceiling leads to the foyer. French doors open the great room to a terrace and courtyard. The forward rooms establish a formal zone enhanced by projecting bays, carved arches, and coffered and beamed ceilings. A private wing that includes the kitchen and morning nook opens to the loggia.

REAR ELEVATION

FIRST FLOOR

SECOND FLOOR

TO ORDER CALL: 1-866-525-9374	PLAN#: DHFB01-3946	*Heritage Pointe*							
TOTAL LIVING	**FIRST FLOOR**	**SECOND FLOOR**	**BONUS ROOM**	**BED**	**BATH**	**WIDTH**	**DEPTH**	**FOUNDATION**	**PRICE CODE**
2766 sq. ft.	1959 sq. ft.	817 sq. ft.	271 sq. ft.	5	3	59'0"	52'0"	Basement or Crawl Space	H

©2005 Frank Betz Associates, Inc.

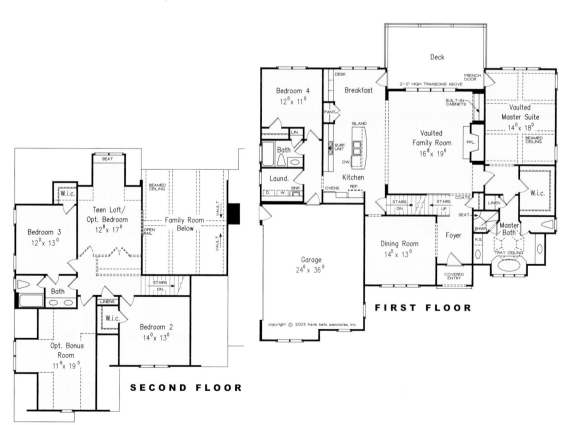

SECOND FLOOR

FIRST FLOOR

The European look of the *Heritage Pointe* would be ideal for a mountain community. A teen loft on the second floor has a window seat and the option to include a closet. The master suite occupies one wing of the home and features a vaulted ceiling. The vaulted family room has built-in bookshelves, a fireplace and views to the rear of the home.

REAR ELEVATION

Keenes Pointe

PLAN#: DHFB01-3940

TO ORDER CALL: 1-866-525-9374

TOTAL LIVING	FIRST FLOOR	SECOND FLOOR	BONUS ROOM	BED	BATH	WIDTH	DEPTH	FOUNDATION	PRICE CODE
2858 sq. ft.	1895 sq. ft.	963 sq. ft.	352 sq. ft.	5	4	54'0"	70'4"	Basement or Crawl Space	H

©2005 Frank Betz Associates, Inc.

The high beamed tray ceiling of the master suite makes the *Keenes Pointe* the perfect home for a mountain or lake home. A rear deck off the kitchen makes entertaining fun and convenient. A suite on the main level offers guests access to a private bath and a walk-in closet. Three additional bedrooms and an optional bonus room complete the second floor.

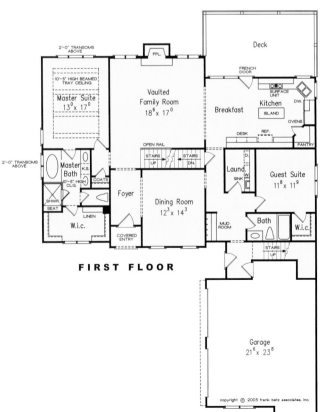

FIRST FLOOR

SECOND FLOOR

TO ORDER CALL: 1-866-525-9374	PLAN#: DHFB01-3746	*Prescott Ridge*

TOTAL LIVING	FIRST FLOOR	SECOND FLOOR	BED	BATH	WIDTH	DEPTH	FOUNDATION	PRICE CODE
2885 sq. ft.	2052 sq. ft.	833 sq. ft.	5	4	59'0"	55'6"	Basement or Crawl Space	H

©2002 Frank Betz Associates, Inc.

FIRST FLOOR

SECOND FLOOR

Original and thoughtful design talent went into every detail of the *Prescott Ridge*. The well-planned kitchen is complete with a cook-top island and double ovens. A window seat creates the back wall of the keeping room, adding charm and comfort to the room. It shares a two-sided fireplace with the neighboring two-story great room.

REAR ELEVATION

Hembree

PLAN#:	TO ORDER CALL:
DHDG01-1111	1-866-525-9374

TOTAL LIVING	FIRST FLOOR	BONUS ROOM	BED	BATH	WIDTH	DEPTH	FOUNDATION	PRICE CODE
2991 sq. ft.	2991 sq. ft.	371 sq. ft.	3	2-1/2	55'7"	90'3.5"	Crawl Space*	F

*Other foundation options available. See page 255

©2005 Donald A. Gardner, Inc.

For families that love large, open living spaces, this home was designed for you. Featuring a great room and family room, as well as outdoor courtyard and lanai, this floor plan boasts spaciousness. The bedrooms are positioned in the rear of the home granting privacy, while living rooms are positioned up front with a completely open feel.

REAR ELEVATION

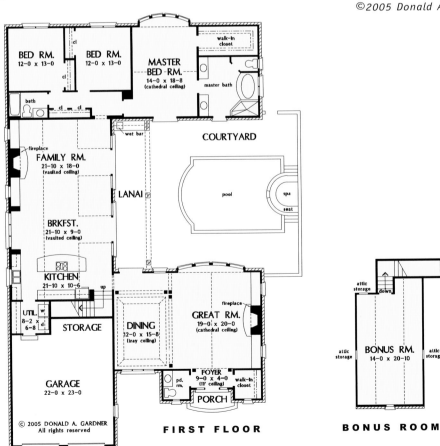

FIRST FLOOR

BONUS ROOM

TO ORDER CALL: 1-866-525-9374	PLAN#: DHDS01-8058	*Porta Rossa*

TOTAL LIVING	FIRST FLOOR	SECOND FLOOR	BED	BATH	WIDTH	DEPTH	FOUNDATION	PRICE CODE
3166 sq. ft.	3166 sq. ft.	N/A	4	3-1/2	67'0"	91'8"	Slab	H

©The Sater Design Collection, Inc.

The carved entry extends an invitation into this view-oriented design. Interior vistas mix it up with sunlight and fresh breezes through the plan, with walls of glass extending living spaces to the outdoors. A high-beamed ceiling, crafted cabinetry and a hearth achieve a colonial character that is seamlessly fused with state-of-the-art style: retreating walls, wide-open rooms and sleek appliances.

REAR ELEVATION

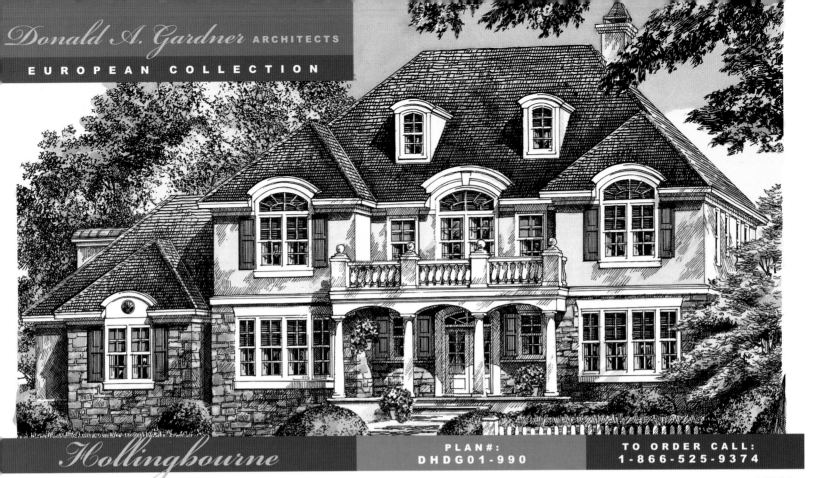

Hollingbourne

PLAN#:
DHDG01-990

TO ORDER CALL:
1-866-525-9374

TOTAL LIVING	FIRST FLOOR	SECOND FLOOR	BONUS ROOM	BED	BATH	WIDTH	DEPTH	FOUNDATION	PRICE CODE
3341 sq. ft.	2062 sq. ft.	1279 sq. ft.	386 sq. ft.	5	4-1/2	73'8"	50'0"	Crawl Space*	G

**Other foundation options available. See page 255*

©2002 Donald A. Gardner, Inc.

Reminiscent of Old-World Manors, this stately home features a stone and stucco exterior. Open, yet with room definition, the interior includes custom-styled elements. A grand staircase leads to a balcony loft, which separates the two-story foyer and great room. Built-ins, a fireplace and French doors enhance the great room, while bay windows extend the master bedroom and breakfast nook.

FIRST FLOOR

REAR ELEVATION

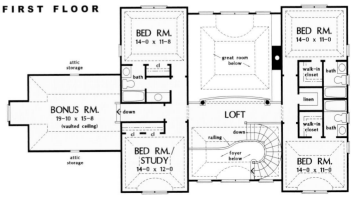

SECOND FLOOR

TO ORDER CALL:
1-866-525-9374

PLAN#:
DHDG01-1046

Oxfordshire

TOTAL LIVING	FIRST FLOOR	SECOND FLOOR	BONUS ROOM	BED	BATH	WIDTH	DEPTH	FOUNDATION	PRICE CODE
3367 sq. ft.	2562 sq. ft.	805 sq. ft.	622 sq. ft.	4	4	87'7"	59'6"	Crawl Space*	G

***Other foundation options available. See page 255**

FIRST FLOOR

SECOND FLOOR

Evoking the Old-World charm of manors, this home showcases stone and a spectacular entrance; columns frame the metal-topped portico. Designed to hold the latest amenities, this floor plan balances formal and informal spaces. Decorative windows usher in light, while columns and built-in cabinetry enhance elegance. A kitchen island, butler's pantry and walk-in pantry/storage make every cook feel like a chef.

REAR ELEVATION

Hearthstone

		PLAN#:	TO ORDER CALL:
		DHFB01-3944	1-866-525-9374

TOTAL LIVING	FIRST FLOOR	SECOND FLOOR	BONUS ROOM	BED	BATH	WIDTH	DEPTH	FOUNDATION	PRICE CODE
3558 sq. ft.	2493 sq. ft.	1065 sq. ft.	277 sq. ft.	4	3-1/2	78'4"	68'0"	Basement, Crawl Space or Slab	I

©2005 Frank Betz Associates, Inc.

Traditional brick and stacked stone beckon you to the *Hearthstone*. Inside, the master suite is on one wing of the home, boasting a large sitting room with a fireplace. The rear porch and deck offer plenty of room for entertaining and relaxing. Three bedrooms and an optional bonus room complete the second level.

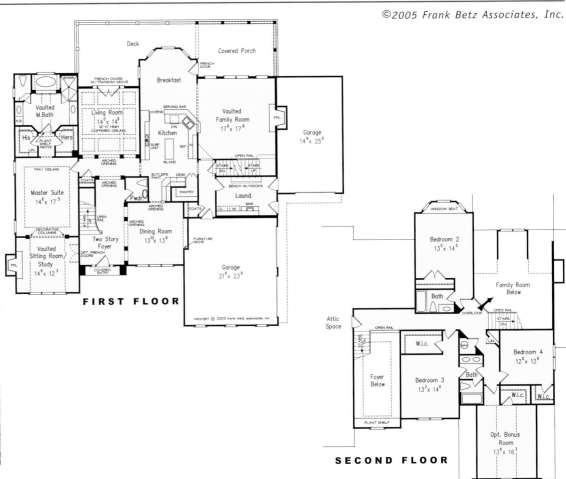

FIRST FLOOR

SECOND FLOOR

REAR ELEVATION

TO ORDER CALL: 1-866-525-9374	PLAN#: DHFB01-3914	*Greywell*

TOTAL LIVING	FIRST FLOOR	SECOND FLOOR	BED	BATH	WIDTH	DEPTH	FOUNDATION	PRICE CODE
3629 sq. ft.	2499 sq. ft.	1130 sq. ft.	5	4	67'6"	69'10"	Basement, Crawl Space or Slab	I

©2004 Frank Betz Associates, Inc.

SECOND FLOOR

FIRST FLOOR

One step inside and it's easy to see that the *Greywell's* character doesn't stop at the curb. The kitchen overlooks a gracious breakfast area, as well as a fire lit keeping room. Coffered ceilings and built-in cabinetry make the family room extra special. A children's retreat makes the perfect playroom or can be used as an additional bedroom.

REAR ELEVATION

Salina

		PLAN#: DHDS01-8043			TO ORDER CALL: 1-866-525-9374			

TOTAL LIVING	FIRST FLOOR	SECOND FLOOR	BED	BATH	WIDTH	DEPTH	FOUNDATION	PRICE CODE
3743 sq. ft.	3743 sq. ft.	N/A	4	3-1/2	80'0"	104'8"	Slab or Opt. Basement	I

©The Sater Design Collection, Inc.

An engaging blend of old and new prevails inside: beamed and coffered ceilings play counterpoint to state-of-the-art amenities — a wet bar that serves private and public zones, cutting-edge culinary appliances in the gourmet kitchen, and a stand-alone media center between the leisure and game rooms. Varied volumes and gently rounded arches define the easy transitions between well-appointed rooms and open spaces.

REAR ELEVATION

FIRST FLOOR

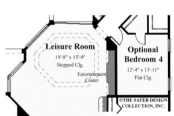

OPT. 4TH BEDROOM

TO ORDER CALL:	PLAN#:	*Flanagan*
1-866-525-9374	DHFB01-1058	

TOTAL LIVING	FIRST FLOOR	SECOND FLOOR	BED	BATH	WIDTH	DEPTH	FOUNDATION	PRICE CODE
3877 sq. ft.	2060 sq. ft.	1817 sq. ft.	5	4-1/2	54'0"	78'4"	Basement, Crawl Space or Slab	J

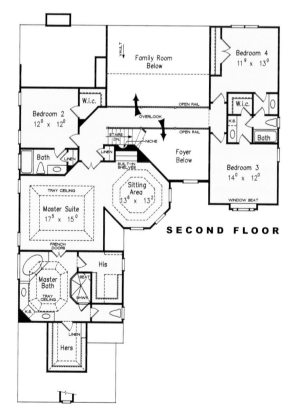

SECOND FLOOR

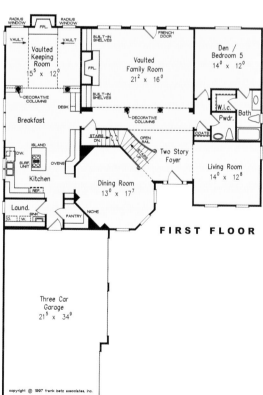

FIRST FLOOR

If your home is your castle, then the *Flanagan* is the design for you. A stunning stone turret gives this plan eye-catching curb appeal. A vaulted keeping room — accentuated by decorative columns — adjoins the kitchen area. The master suite earns its name featuring a uniquely shaped sitting area.

REAR ELEVATION

Royal Country

	PLAN#:				TO ORDER CALL:
	DHDS01-8001				1-866-525-9374

TOTAL LIVING	FIRST FLOOR	SECOND FLOOR	BED	BATH	WIDTH	DEPTH	FOUNDATION	PRICE CODE
3977 sq. ft.	2834 sq. ft.	1143 sq. ft.	4	3-1/2	85'0"	76'8"	Slab or Opt. Basement	I

©The Sater Design Collection, Inc.

Carved pilasters, columns and scrolled pediments highlight the refined spirit of this home. Built-in shelves frame an entertainment center in the leisure room, and anchor an open arrangement of casual space with the morning nook and the gourmet kitchen. A spectacular yet comfortable winding staircase draws family members and guests up to the secondary sleeping quarters on the upper level.

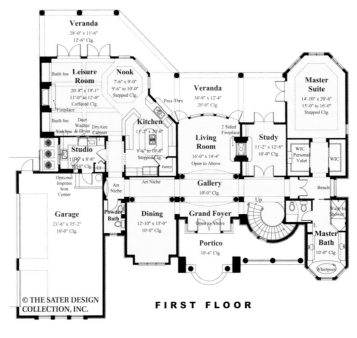

FIRST FLOOR

© THE SATER DESIGN COLLECTION, INC.

SECOND FLOOR

| TO ORDER CALL:
1-866-525-9374 | | PLAN#:
DHDS01-8010 | | | *Capucina* | | | | | |

TOTAL LIVING	FIRST FLOOR	SECOND FLOOR	BONUS ROOM	BED	BATH	WIDTH	DEPTH	FOUNDATION	PRICE CODE
4011 sq. ft.	2855 sq. ft.	1156 sq. ft.	371 sq. ft.	4	4-1/2	71'6"	83'0"	Slab or Opt. Basement	I

©The Sater Design Collection, Inc.

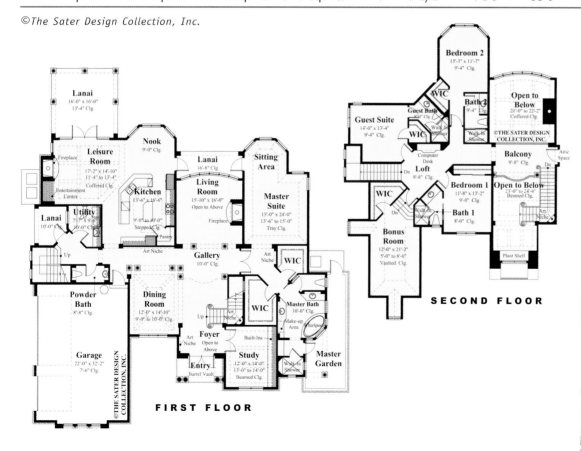

FIRST FLOOR

SECOND FLOOR

Glass panels and a fanlight enhance the sculpted entry of the façade. An open arrangement of the central living space, gallery and formal dining room permits views of the back property through a two-story bow window. French doors open the leisure room to the outdoors, while the morning bay accesses a lanai shared with the master suite's private sitting bay.

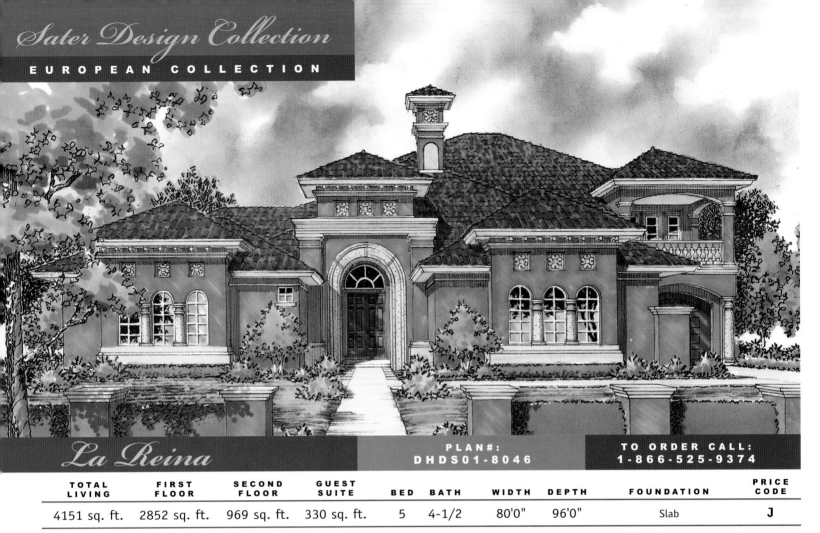

La Reina

PLAN#:
DHDS01-8046

TO ORDER CALL:
1-866-525-9374

TOTAL LIVING	FIRST FLOOR	SECOND FLOOR	GUEST SUITE	BED	BATH	WIDTH	DEPTH	FOUNDATION	PRICE CODE
4151 sq. ft.	2852 sq. ft.	969 sq. ft.	330 sq. ft.	5	4-1/2	80'0"	96'0"	Slab	J

The elaborate entry turret opens to portico and courtyard, which leads to the formal entry of the home. The foyer opens directly to the grand room and, through an arched opening, to the formal dining room. Glass bayed walls in the central living area and in the study help meld inside and outside spaces.

FIRST FLOOR

SECOND FLOOR

REAR ELEVATION

TO ORDER CALL:
1-866-525-9374

PLAN#:
DHGA01-03257

Mon Chateau

TOTAL LIVING	FIRST FLOOR	SECOND FLOOR	BONUS ROOM	BED	BATH	WIDTH	DEPTH	FOUNDATION	PRICE CODE
4396 sq. ft.	3209 sq. ft.	1187 sq. ft.	264 sq. ft.	4	4-1/2	82'0"	76'5"	Basement or Crawl Space	0

Home photographed may differ from construction documents.

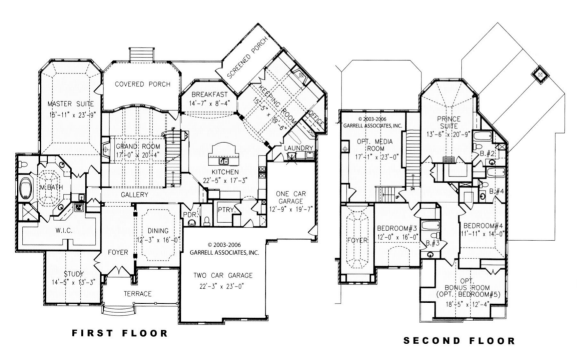

FIRST FLOOR

SECOND FLOOR

This design was developed for the discerning homeowner who knows the value of a well-designed plan. Years of research have shaped the spaces within this plan and have made it a most popular choice. Strong features like the angled keeping room and oversized master suite enhance the flow of modern life. The second floor offers three bedroom suites and an optional media and bonus room.

REAR ELEVATION

Port Royal Way

PLAN#: DHDS01-6635							**TO ORDER CALL:** 1-866-525-9374		

TOTAL LIVING	FIRST FLOOR	SECOND FLOOR	BED	BATH	WIDTH	DEPTH	FOUNDATION	PRICE CODE
6312 sq. ft.	4760 sq. ft.	1552 sq. ft.	5	6-1/2	98'0"	103'8"	Slab	M

©The Sater Design Collection, Inc.

A spectacular blend of arch top windows, glass doors and balusters hint at the captivating design within this estate home. The double door entry leads to the grand foyer where columns and archways grace the view through the formal living room. A two-story ceiling, two-sided fireplace and three pairs of French doors add to the drama of this open floor plan.

REAR ELEVATION

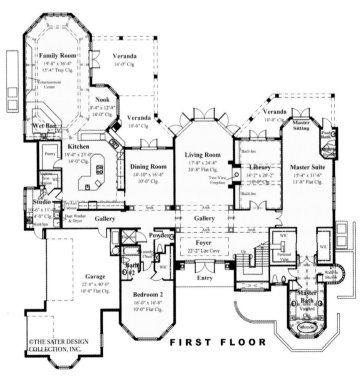

FIRST FLOOR

SECOND FLOOR

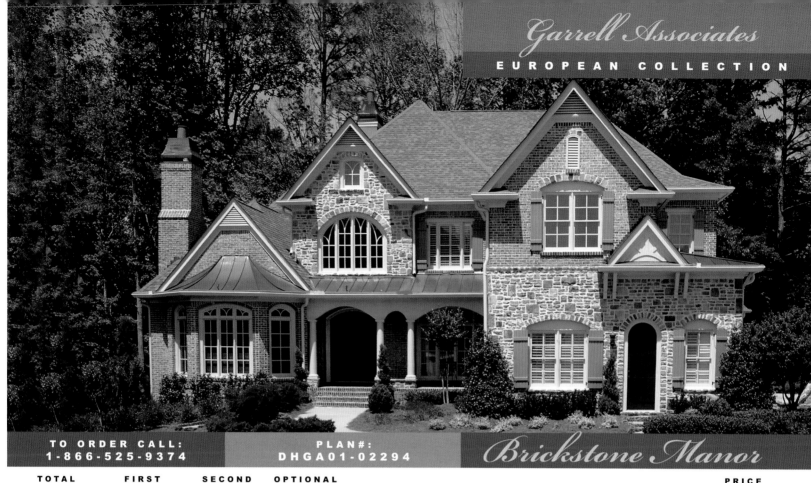

	TO ORDER CALL: 1-866-525-9374	PLAN#: DHGA01-02294		*Brickstone Manor*

TOTAL LIVING	FIRST FLOOR	SECOND FLOOR	OPTIONAL SITTING	BED	BATH	WIDTH	DEPTH	FOUNDATION	PRICE CODE
6750 sq. ft.	4005 sq. ft.	2745 sq. ft.	158 sq. ft.	5	4-1/2	87'3"	85'8"	Basement	O

©*Garrell Associates, Inc.*

Home photographed may differ from construction documents.

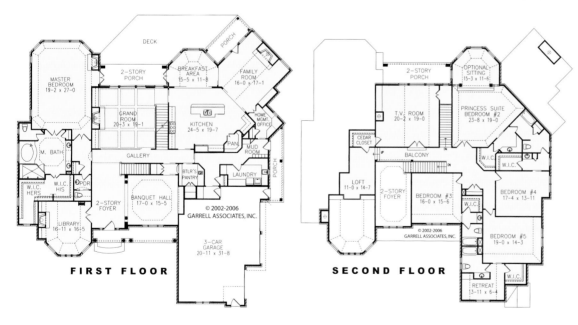

FIRST FLOOR

SECOND FLOOR

Old-World charm and warmth invite you to the front porch of this Normandy-style home. A spacious banquet hall and gourmet kitchen opens to a breakfast room and angled keeping room with fireplace. A home office, laundry room, mud room and butler's pantry make up the service hall. The master suite provides comfort and privacy. Perfect for a large family, the second floor is complete with four bedroom suites, a loft and TV room.

REAR ELEVATION

American Classic

Gastonia -
FRANK BETZ ASSOCIATES - See page 152

Gastonia - **DINING ROOM**

How does a classic… become a classic?

A sense of style is certainly important, a well-known standard of architectural proportions is also essential. But we like to think that classics are formed by endurance. By time. These designs have been created with the highest, most established, standards of style. The simple, harmonious lines of wide, expansive porches, lovely gables and traditional dormers; the quiet beauty of flowing, open floor plans; strong, elegant columns and impressive built-in cabinetry; wide, open gourmet kitchens and luxuriant, secluded master suites—these are the elements that have endured over time. Explore these American Classics and find a home of exquisite balance and refinement.

Satchwell - **GREAT ROOM**

DONALD A. GARDNER ARCHITECTS - See page 158

AMERICAN CLASSIC

Hopkins

© 1995 FRANK BETZ ASSOCIATES, INC.

PLAN# DHFB01-853   **1-866-525-9374**

Many distinctive design elements come together in the *Hopkins* to make an attractive and highly-functional design. From its traditional exterior and covered front porch to its upscale interior amenities, this home has it all! The kitchen and breakfast areas connect with a two-story family room making interaction easy from one room to the next. A main-floor bedroom can be used as a home office or den. An optional loft has been designed for the upper level that can serve a multitude of purposes. A playroom, fitness area, or craft room would all fit ideally into this space. Two additional bedrooms are located on the second floor and share a Jack-and-Jill bath.

FAMILY ROOM (above & right) — The family room is designed for gathering and conversation, opening into the breakfast room and kitchen.

KITCHEN/NOOK — The red-green-gold color scheme permeates all three areas, helping visually unite the space.

KITCHEN — The warm-colored cabinetry and green-tile backsplash echo the colors of the outdoors, which is easily accessible throught the breakfast room.

MASTER BEDROOM — Spacious and serene, the master bedroom features a neutral palette with sitting areas and a beautiful tray ceiling.

MASTER BATH — A decorative ceiling, glass shower and garden tub pamper the owners with style and space.

LIVING ROOM — The sweeping staircase opens into a vaulted living room, creating a dramatic entry into the home.

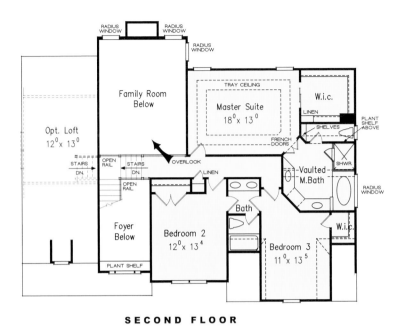

SECOND FLOOR

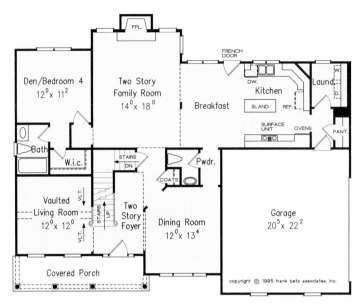

FIRST FLOOR

LOFT — This optional space is the perfect location for a home office or a homework station.

REAR ELEVATION

TO ORDER CALL: 1-866-525-9374		PLAN#: DHFB01-853		*Hopkins*						
TOTAL LIVING	**FIRST FLOOR**	**SECOND FLOOR**	**BONUS ROOM**	**BED**	**BATH**	**WIDTH**	**DEPTH**	**FOUNDATION**		**PRICE CODE**
2430 sq. ft.	1415 sq. ft.	1015 sq. ft.	169 sq. ft.	4	3-1/2	54'0"	43'4"	Basement or Crawl Space		G

Home photographed may differ from construction documents.

Edgewater

© 2003 DONALD A. GARDNER, INC.

PLAN# DHDG01-1009   1-866-525-9374

For the family that loves elegant, one-story living, the *Edgewater* is home. With several versatile rooms and both formal and casual entertaining spaces, this floor plan provides years of quality living. This home has plenty of Craftsman character with a low-maintenance exterior. Doubled columns and stone accents create architectural interest.

Columns and a tray ceiling distinguish the dining room, while double doors open into the study/bedroom. Art niches, fireplaces and built-in cabinetry add beauty and convenience. The kitchen has a handy pass-thru to the great room. The spacious deck accommodates outdoor living.

The master suite has a bay sitting area and French doors that lead to the deck. The master bath is equipped with a double vanity, private privy, garden tub and shower with a shelf and seat.

FOYER — The overhead clerestory and side transoms create a stunning frame around the center door, while also ushering natural light throughout the foyer.

KITCHEN/BREAKFAST NOOK — Completely open, the kitchen and breakfast nook overflow into one another and provide an easy transition into the family and living rooms.

KITCHEN — The kitchen has a handy pass-thru to the great room and features angled countertops to divide the kitchen from the breakfast room.

FAMILY ROOM — Tucked away off the breakfast room, the family room is complete with a fireplace, built-in shelves and cathedral ceiling.

FAMILY ROOM — The stone fireplace and built-in cabinetry provide convenience and add a luxurious feel to the room.

DINING ROOM — Columns and a tray ceiling distinguish the dining room, creating a formal room for entertaining or enjoying meals with the whole family.

LIVING ROOM — Transoms and French doors bathe the room with natural light as well as providing stunning views of the backyard.

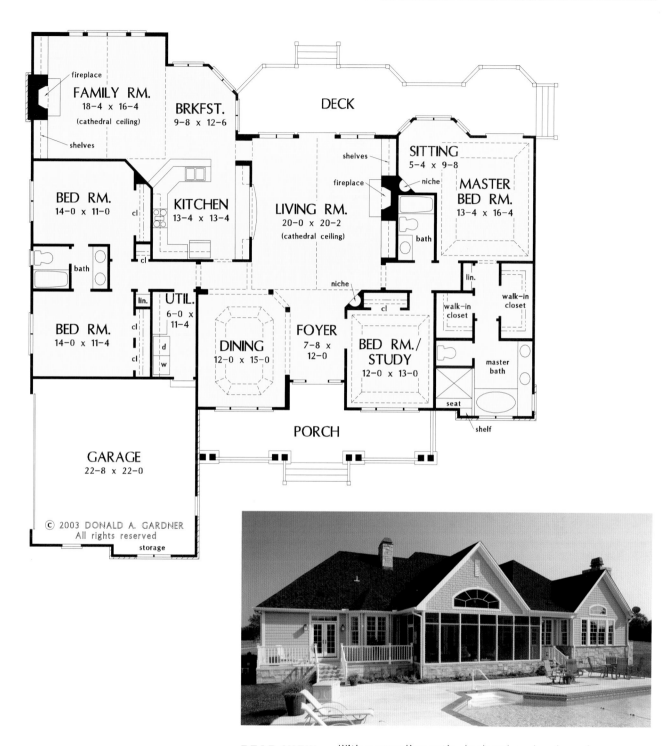

FAMILY RM.
18-4 x 16-4
(cathedral ceiling)

fireplace

shelves

BRKFST.
9-8 x 12-6

DECK

shelves

SITTING
5-4 x 9-8

fireplace

niche

MASTER BED RM.
13-4 x 16-4

BED RM.
14-0 x 11-0

cl

KITCHEN
13-4 x 13-4

LIVING RM.
20-0 x 20-2
(cathedral ceiling)

bath

cl

bath

lin.

walk-in closet

niche

walk-in closet

BED RM.
14-0 x 11-4

lin.

cl

UTIL.
6-0 x 11-4

cl

d

w

DINING
12-0 x 15-0

FOYER
7-8 x 12-0

niche

cl

BED RM./ STUDY
12-0 x 13-0

master bath

seat

shelf

PORCH

GARAGE
22-8 x 22-0

© 2003 DONALD A. GARDNER
All rights reserved

storage

REAR VIEW — With a sprawling patio, backyard pool and spacious screened porch, entertaining spaces are plentiful in this striking rear exterior.

*Other foundation options available. See page 255

TO ORDER CALL: 1-866-525-9374	PLAN#: DHDG01-1009	*Edgewater*						
TOTAL LIVING	FIRST FLOOR	BONUS ROOM	BED	BATH	WIDTH	DEPTH	FOUNDATION	PRICE CODE
2818 sq. ft.	2818 sq. ft.	N/A	4	3	70'0"	69'10"	Crawl Space*	F

Home photographed may differ from construction documents.

AMERICAN CLASSIC

Windsong

© 1998 FRANK BETZ ASSOCIATES, INC.

PLAN# DHFB01-1200   **1-866-525-9374**

A spectacular two-story foyer — with a tray ceiling and an art niche — is just the beginning of this well-planned design. The living and dining rooms border the foyer and share common space making entertaining comfortable and easy. The kitchen and breakfast areas adjoin a two-story family room with a fireplace and built-in cabinetry. The master suite lives up to its name with a private sitting area. The luxurious bath offers his-and-her closets, a separate tub and shower and dual sinks. A tandem three-car garage leaves plenty of utility storage. Three additional bedrooms are located on the second floor.

DINING ROOM — Wainscoting and crown molding welcome visitors with this warm dining space.

NOOK/KITCHEN — A tile floor, center island and rich cabinetry make this kitchen a room to be enjoyed.

SUNROOM — A brick floor and a wall of windows provide the perfect backdrop for this sunroom.

MASTER BEDROOM — This spacious bedroom, features a tray ceiling and a sitting area.

MASTER BATH — Luxuriousness awaits in this master bath which features dual sinks and a separate tub and shower.

KID'S ROOM — Creative furniture and murals create a whimsical room for the home's youngest inhabitants.

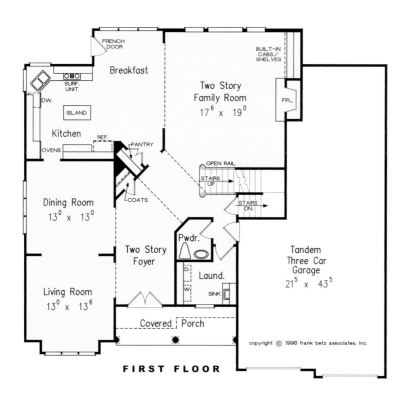

FIRST FLOOR

- FRENCH DOOR
- Breakfast
- SURF. UNIT
- DW.
- ISLAND
- Kitchen
- OVENS
- REF.
- PANTRY
- COATS
- Dining Room 13⁰ x 13⁰
- Two Story Foyer
- Pwdr.
- D. W.
- Laund.
- SINK
- Living Room 13⁰ x 13⁶
- Covered Porch
- Two Story Family Room 17⁶ x 19⁰
- BUILT-IN CABS./SHELVES
- FPL.
- OPEN RAIL
- STAIRS UP
- STAIRS DN.
- Tandem Three Car Garage 21⁵ x 43⁵
- copyright © 1998 frank betz associates, inc.

OPT. SUNROOM

- FPL.
- Opt. Sunroom 14⁴ x 14²

REAR ELEVATION

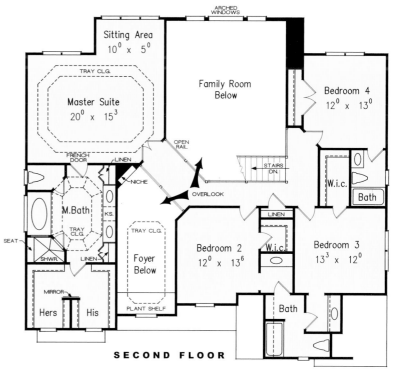

SECOND FLOOR

- ARCHED WINDOWS
- Sitting Area 10⁰ x 5⁰
- TRAY CLG.
- Master Suite 20⁰ x 15³
- Family Room Below
- Bedroom 4 12⁰ x 13⁰
- FRENCH DOOR
- LINEN
- NICHE
- OPEN RAIL
- STAIRS DN.
- W.i.c.
- Bath
- M.Bath
- KS.
- TRAY CLG.
- SEAT
- SHWR.
- LINEN
- OVERLOOK
- TRAY CLG.
- Foyer Below
- Bedroom 2 12⁰ x 13⁶
- LINEN
- W.i.c.
- Bedroom 3 13³ x 12⁰
- MIRROR
- Hers
- His
- PLANT SHELF
- Bath

TO ORDER CALL: 1-866-525-9374

PLAN#: DHFB01-1200

Windsong

TOTAL LIVING	FIRST FLOOR	SECOND FLOOR	BED	BATH	WIDTH	DEPTH	FOUNDATION	PRICE CODE
3068 sq. ft.	1473 sq. ft.	1595 sq. ft.	4	3-1/2	53'0"	49'0"	Basement or Crawl Space	H

Home photographed may differ from construction documents.

©1998 Frank Betz Associates, Inc.

WWW.DESIGNER-DREAMHOMES.COM | 141

Yankton

© 2001 DONALD A. GARDNER, INC.

PLAN# DHDG01-933   1-866-525-9374

This design takes a little of the Southeast and shares it with the rest of the country through this stunning façade. Twin dormers separate two sets of matching gables, and exterior windows are accented with metal roofs.

When walking inside, the lavish foyer immediately spills into the open dining room. Columns are used to define the dining room, while a tray ceiling elegantly draws the eye upward. Gracefully flowing into the great room and adjacent kitchen, you'll want to serve all formal meals in this room.

The kitchen is sizeable enough for more than one chef, while a pass-thru to the great room opens the entire space. Windows surround the breakfast room, granting natural light to this casual space. French doors and transoms also help to brighten the great room, while a fireplace, cathedral ceiling and built-in shelves add architectural interest.

DINING ROOM — Windows and transoms keep this dining room open and bright.

GREAT ROOM — French doors and overhead transoms brighten the great room, while the handy kitchen pass-thru keeps conversation flowing from room to room.

KITCHEN — The breakfast room and kitchen seamlessly flow into one another to simplify mealtime.

GREAT ROOM — An overhead clerestory and stone fireplace enhance the great room, while built-in shelves provide the perfect spot to display family photos and keepsakes.

GREAT ROOM — Visible through the foyer, the great room is a stunning focal point when entering the home.

REAR VIEW — Gables and decorative windows take curb appeal around to the back of the home.

MASTER BATH — The relaxing master bath includes a separate shower and tub, for true indulgence.

MASTER BEDROOM — Relaxation is easy in the master bedroom, as it accesses the rear porch and has a vaulted ceiling to grant vertical volume.

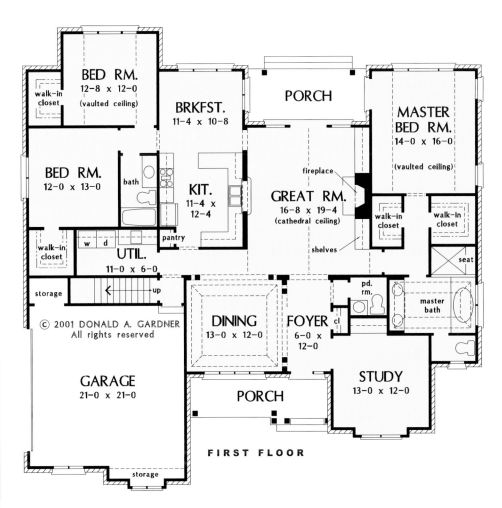

BED RM.
12-8 x 12-0
(vaulted ceiling)

walk-in closet

BRKFST.
11-4 x 10-8

PORCH

MASTER BED RM.
14-0 x 16-0
(vaulted ceiling)

BED RM.
12-0 x 13-0

bath

KIT.
11-4 x 12-4

fireplace

GREAT RM.
16-8 x 19-4
(cathedral ceiling)

walk-in closet

walk-in closet

pantry

shelves

seat

walk-in closet

w   d

UTIL.
11-0 x 6-0

storage

up

pd. rm.

master bath

DINING
13-0 x 12-0

FOYER
6-0 x 12-0

cl

© 2001 DONALD A. GARDNER
All rights reserved

GARAGE
21-0 x 21-0

PORCH

STUDY
13-0 x 12-0

storage

FIRST FLOOR

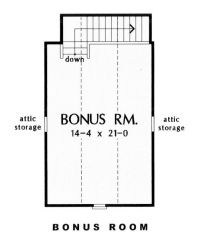

attic storage

BONUS RM.
14-4 x 21-0

attic storage

down

BONUS ROOM

REAR PORCH — By adding a covered porch, this homeowner created an exciting outdoor gathering spot.

TO ORDER CALL:
1-866-525-9374

PLAN#:
DHDG01-933

Yankton

TOTAL LIVING	FIRST FLOOR	BONUS ROOM	BED	BATH	WIDTH	DEPTH	FOUNDATION	PRICE CODE
2330 sq. ft.	2330 sq. ft.	364 sq. ft.	3	2-1/2	62'3"	60'6"	Crawl Space	E

Home photographed may differ from construction documents.

AMERICAN CLASSIC

Covington Ridge

© 2003 FRANK BETZ ASSOCIATES, INC.

PLAN# **DHFB01-3792**   **1-866-525-9374**

Inventive and creative design elements set the *Covington Ridge* apart from other more common plans. Beginning with the stunning wraparound porch and the brick and siding exterior, this plan would be a welcome addition to any neighborhood. The kitchen overlooks a warm and inviting keeping room, making an ideal location for laid-back time with family or friends. A work area serves as the command center of the home, giving homeowners designated space for a computer and household paperwork. The main-floor bedroom can easily double as a home office. No details were overlooked in this smart design — decorative columns and built-in shelves are incorporated to add charm and character.

KITCHEN — Hardwood floors, wood cabinets and black countertops combine to make a warm and inviting kitchen.

DINING ROOM — The golden yellow walls complement the dark furniture making this a special room for entertaining.

KEEPING ROOM — The serving bar from the kitchen overlooks the keeping room which allows for easy traffic flow from one room to the other.

FAMILY ROOM — The spacious family room with the high ceiling gives an open feeling to the home.

MASTER BEDROOM — The tray ceilings and rear wall of windows make this a special retreat for the homeowners.

MASTER BATH — Separate sinks, tub and shower allow each resident ample space.

KID'S ROOM — Spacious secondary rooms give families plenty of room to grow.

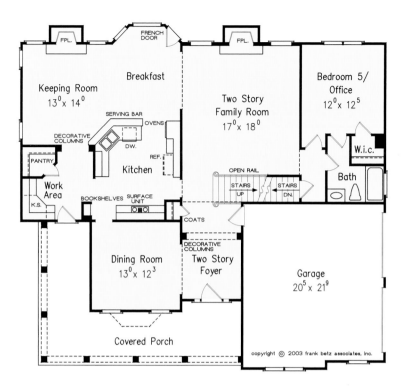

FIRST FLOOR

REAR ELEVATION

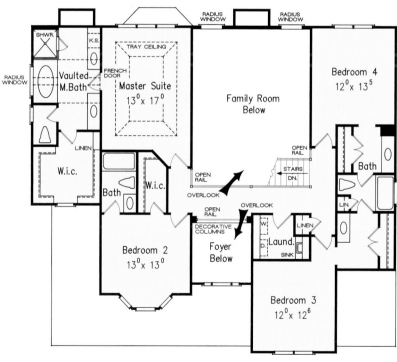

SECOND FLOOR

TO ORDER CALL: 1-866-525-9374		**PLAN#:** DHFB01-3792			*Covington Ridge*				

TOTAL LIVING	FIRST FLOOR	SECOND FLOOR	BED	BATH	WIDTH	DEPTH	FOUNDATION	PRICE CODE
3041 sq. ft.	1558 sq. ft.	1483 sq. ft.	5	4	53'0"	48'0"	Basement or Crawl Space	H

Home photographed may differ from construction documents.

©2003 Frank Betz Associates, Inc.

© 1994 DONALD A. GARDNER, INC.

PLAN# DHDG01-331   1-866-525-9374

Sometimes with a larger floor plan, the feeling of an intimate, cozy home gets lost in translation. The *Milford* fulfills the need for a bigger home yet includes a layout designed to unite families. The great room is strategically located in the middle of the house, assuring a central locale for family gatherings. The cathedral ceiling, fireplace and rear-porch access grant striking details to the room, while custom molding and built-in bookshelves enhance its uniqueness.

Designed to promote a natural traffic flow, the kitchen uses angled countertops to create a partition between the great and breakfast rooms. Throughout the rest of the home, large, open entryways enable the rooms to spill out into one another, eliminating the need for doors.

GREAT ROOM — Custom molding around the fireplace and built-in cabinets showcase architectural details in the great room.

KITCHEN — All-white cabinetry and countertops provide a sleek and clean look to the kitchen.

GREAT ROOM — French doors and a wide entry into the kitchen grant luxury to the elegant great room.

REAR VIEW — Skylights over the covered porch and breakfast room invite Mother Nature indoors during mealtime.

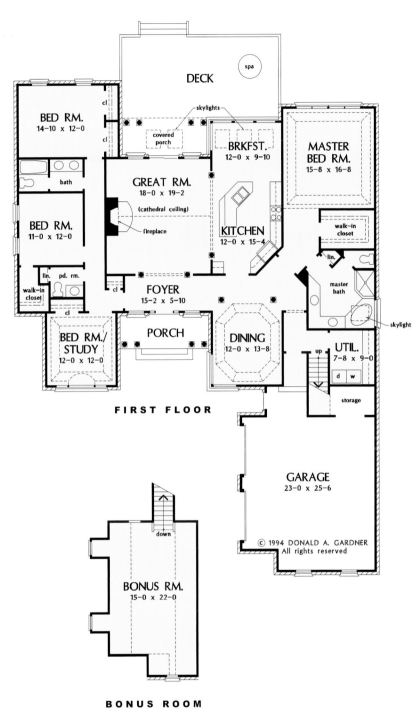

FIRST FLOOR

BONUS ROOM

*Other foundation options available. See page 255

	TO ORDER CALL: 1-866-525-9374	PLAN#: DHDG01-331	*Milford*						
TOTAL LIVING	FIRST FLOOR	BONUS ROOM	BED	BATH	WIDTH	DEPTH	FOUNDATION		PRICE CODE
2625 sq. ft.	2625 sq. ft.	447 sq. ft.	4	2-1/2	63'1"	82'7"	Crawl Space*		F

Home photographed may differ from construction documents.

© 2002 FRANK BETZ ASSOCIATES, INC.

PLAN# DHFB01-3721   1-866-525-9374

Smaller homes don't have to lack upscale amenities! The *Gastonia* includes many special features often hard to find even in larger homes. The master suite has a comfortable sitting room, large enough for lounging furniture. However, if a fourth bedroom is a higher priority, this space can be easily converted to accommodate it. Each secondary bedroom features a walk-in closet. An island serves as the center point of the kitchen and helps with meal preparation. Decorative columns and an art niche give the main floor extra flavor for decorating. A sink is designed into the laundry room; a practical and useful added feature.

GUEST ROOM — Built-in cabinets provide a place for collectibles in this equestrian themed sitting room/bedroom.

DINING ROOM — Custom molding and a large transom grace the formal dining room and a mirrored wall in the foyer gives the area a dramatic flair.

KITCHEN — An island serves as the center point of the kitchen, convenient for meal preparation.

REAR VIEW

GREAT ROOM — With views to the outdoors, the great room features an intimate sitting area beside built-in cabinetry.

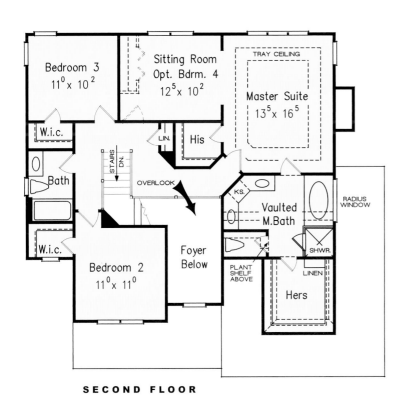

SECOND FLOOR

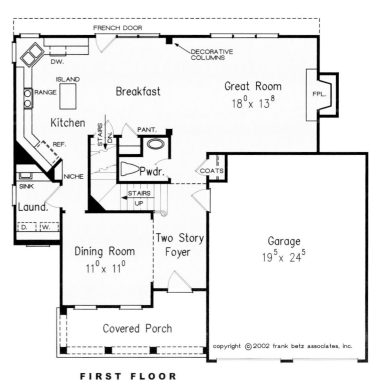

FIRST FLOOR

TO ORDER CALL: 1-866-525-9374	PLAN#: DHFB01-3721	*Gastonia*					

TOTAL LIVING	FIRST FLOOR	SECOND FLOOR	BED	BATH	WIDTH	DEPTH	FOUNDATION	PRICE CODE
2040 sq. ft.	935 sq. ft.	1105 sq. ft.	4	2-1/2	44'0"	39'0"	Basement, Crawl Space or Slab	G

Home photographed may differ from construction documents.

© THE SATER DESIGN COLLECTION, INC.

PLAN# DHDS01-7065   **1-866-525-9374**

The picturesque porch, lined with columns and arches, sets off decorative shutters and dormers. Inside the warm welcome continues with an open floor plan that encourages traffic flow from both wings of the home. At the center, the great room features a coffered ceiling, built-ins and open access to the kitchen and dining room. A two-sided fireplace, shared with the study, adds a cozy touch to the spacious room. Three sets of French doors opening to the back porch extend the living space outside.

A split-floor plan ensures privacy for the homeowner and guests alike. The master retreat features a luxe bath, specialty ceiling and French doors to back porch. On the opposite side of the home, two secondary bedrooms share a full bath. An optional bonus room offers many options.

KITCHEN — A wraparound eating bar connects the great room to the kitchen. A center work island, built-in work desk and easy access to the dining room will please cooks of all levels.

GREAT ROOM — The substantial great room features a coffered ceiling, built-ins and open access to the kitchen and dining rooms. The great room and study share a double-sided fireplace, and both rooms boast French door access to the rear porch.

MASTER BATH — An indulgent walk-in shower and whirlpool-soaking tub create a spa-like atmosphere in the master bath.

MASTER BEDROOM — A relaxing retreat, the master bedroom features a bay window, French doors opening to the back porch and a stylish tray ceiling.

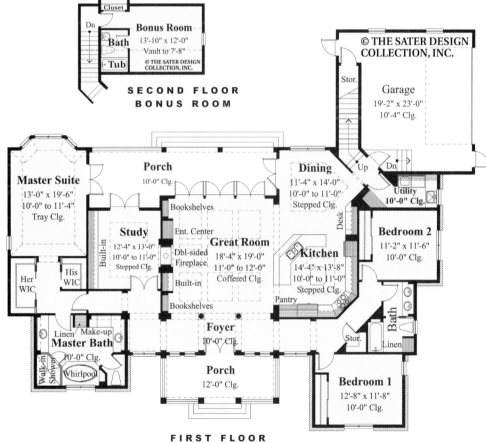

SECOND FLOOR BONUS ROOM

Bonus Room
13'-10" x 12'-0"
Vault to 7'-8"
© THE SATER DESIGN COLLECTION, INC.

FIRST FLOOR

REAR VIEW — Friends and family alike will enjoy the comfort of the spacious back porch — and taking a dip in the pool.

| | TO ORDER CALL: 1-866-525-9374 | | PLAN#: DHDS01-7065 | | *Lexington* | | |

TOTAL LIVING	FIRST FLOOR	BONUS ROOM	BED	BATH	WIDTH	DEPTH	FOUNDATION	PRICE CODE
2454 sq. ft.	2454 sq. ft.	256 sq. ft.	3	2	80'6"	66'6"	Crawl Space/Opt. Slab	F

Home photographed may differ from construction documents.

©*The Sater Design Collection, Inc.*

© CORNERSTONE DESIGNS, LLC

PLAN# DHCS01-M4725A4S-1   1-866-525-9374

The ultimate Victorian farmhouse, the *Astoria* perfectly expresses a luxurious, yet casual lifestyle. The sculptural façade and expansive verandas create an image of comfort and warm welcome.

A dramatic 80-foot view axis through the rotunda to the family room fireplace greets you on entry. The convenient circular floor plan provides easy access to the den and formal living room, while connecting the kitchen and formal dining via the butlery. The covered outdoor dining and BBQ porch connect the family living areas to the outdoors.

The rotunda's circular stair leads you to the spacious master suite retreat. A guest suite, two children's suites sharing the turreted play loft, and a large media room with popcorn kitchen complete the upper floor.

The *Astoria's* traditional beauty highlights a popular floor plan designed for flexible family living.

FAMILY ROOM — The soaring fireplace anchors the family room, flanked by built-ins. Banks of multi-paned windows flood the space with light.

KITCHEN — A grand opening frames the intimately detailed kitchen. The beamed ceiling and cozy niches of the stone-topped island convey an elegant feel.

LIVING ROOM — The traditional mantel, wainscots and ceiling coves distinguish the living room. Its French doors mirror the den across the entry hall.

REAR VIEW — The octagonal rear porch makes a luxurious connection to the outdoors, complete with skylights, fireplace and barbecue.

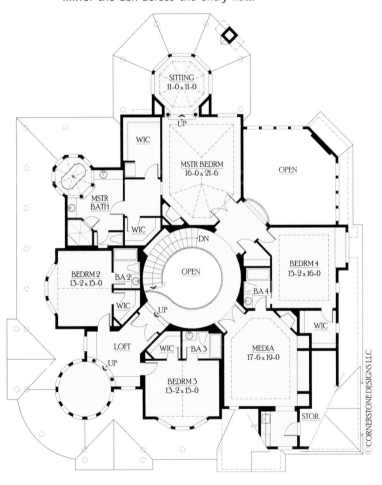

SECOND FLOOR

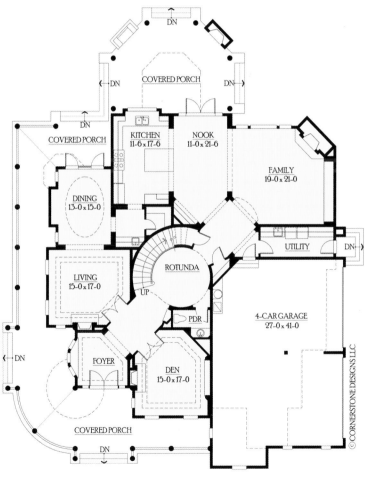

FIRST FLOOR

TO ORDER CALL: 1-866-525-9374	PLAN#: DHCS01-M4725A4S-1	*Astoria*

TOTAL LIVING	FIRST FLOOR	SECOND FLOOR	BED	BATH	WIDTH	DEPTH	FOUNDATION	PRICE CODE
5250 sq. ft.	2375 sq. ft.	2875 sq. ft.	4	4-1/2	71'0"	92'0"	Crawl Space	J

Home photographed may differ from construction documents.

© 2001 DONALD A. GARDNER ARCHITECTS

PLAN# **DHDG01-967** **1-866-525-9374**

Welcome on any streetscape, the *Satchwell's* inviting exterior is an elegant blend. Stone, siding and graceful arches contrast with high gables to create instant curb appeal. Columns create a welcoming entryway onto the front porch.

Indoors, architectural details abound. Decorative transoms and several French doors flood the home with natural light, while ceiling treatments in nearly every room lend drama and interest. The side-entry garage accentuates the exciting exterior, while the utility room just inside the garage allows room for dirty shoes and laundry.

The dining room is an entertainer's dream. Columns define the entrance just off the foyer, while wainscoting and a tray ceiling add flair. Perfect for formal meals and showcasing fine china, this room instantly commands respect.

GREAT ROOM — By combining the grandeur of a cathedral ceiling with the coziness of a fireplace surrounded by built-ins and custom molding, the great room is both relaxed and stunning at the same time.

KITCHEN — Honey-colored cabinetry combines with granite countertops to showcase stainless-steel appliances.

REAR VIEW — Twin windows, an elegant gable and a screened porch create a welcoming rear exterior.

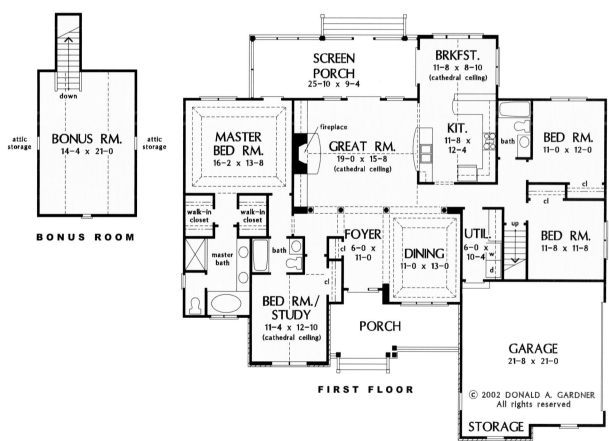

*Other foundation options available. See page 255

TOTAL LIVING	FIRST FLOOR	BONUS ROOM	BED	BATH	WIDTH	DEPTH	FOUNDATION	PRICE CODE
2097 sq. ft.	2097 sq. ft.	352 sq. ft.	4	3	64'10"	59'6"	Crawl Space*	E

Home photographed may differ from construction documents.

©2001 Donald A. Gardner Architects, Inc.

Bainbridge

© THE SATER DESIGN COLLECTION, INC.

PLAN# DHDS01-7051   **1-866-525-9374**

This Victorian inspired home offers a generous interior with flexible rooms and a seamless boundary with the outdoors. The foyer opens to the great room, which is centered by a high-coffered ceiling and a brick fireplace. Ideal for relaxing, the great room also features a wall of glass doors that open to a covered porch. Arches define the casual living spaces, accenting bookcases and an open counter shared by the kitchen. Arranged to provide cozy places to entertain, this open living space can easily host an intimate evening for two or an elaborate party. A split-floor plan ensures privacy for guests and the homeowners alike. The right side includes a powder room, laundry room and two secondary bedrooms. Bordering the left wing is a study and the spacious master suite.

DINING ROOM — Defined by columns and a recessed tin ceiling, the dining room is located near the kitchen and enjoys front porch views.

GREAT ROOM VIEWS — Three sets of glass doors and repeating arches opening to the kitchen add charm to the generous great room. Molded columns flank a cabinet-style eating bar perfect for quick snacks.

KITCHEN — A natural gathering place, the kitchen features a stainless-steel double oven, center prep island and plenty of storage space. The laundry and dining room are conveniently located just through the archway.

REAR VIEW — Glass doors connect the casual living area with the outdoors — a wonderful place to enjoy poolside views while dining.

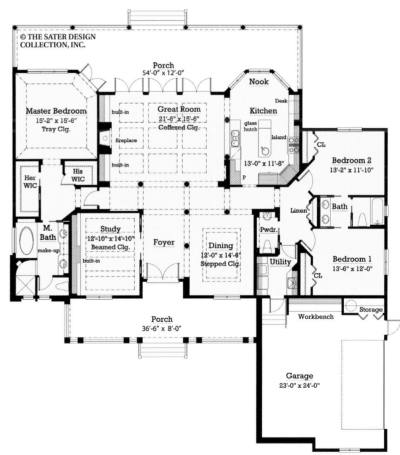

NOOK — Perfect for enjoying morning coffee and catching up with friends and family, the nook is a bright and airy gathering spot.

TO ORDER CALL: 1-866-525-9374		PLAN#: DHDS01-7051		*Bainbridge*					
TOTAL LIVING	**FIRST FLOOR**	**SECOND FLOOR**	**BED**	**BATH**	**WIDTH**	**DEPTH**	**FOUNDATION**	**PRICE CODE**
2555 sq. ft.	2555 sq. ft.	N/A	3	2-1/2	70'6"	76'6"	Crawl Space	G

Home photographed may differ from construction documents.

©*The Sater Design Collection, Inc.*

AMERICAN CLASSIC

Jamestowne

© 1999 DONALD A. GARDNER, INC.

PLAN# DHDG01-828   1-866-525-9374

A prominent center gable and an inviting front porch create excellent curb appeal for this charming two-story family home.

A commanding balcony that overlooks the two-story foyer as well as the two-story great room provides an impressive welcome. Elegant columns mark entry to both the dining room and great room. The generously proportioned kitchen features a nearby pantry and is open to the breakfast room and great room for easy entertaining and family togetherness.

Located on the first floor, the master bedroom enjoys a tray ceiling, back-porch access, a private bath and ample closet space. Upstairs, three more bedrooms share a spacious bath.

GREAT ROOM — Built-in shelves, a balcony, French doors and a two-story stone fireplace are some of the custom details found in the great room.

DINING ROOM — Wainscoting and built-ins grant intrigue to the dining room, making it an optimal place to enjoy meals or entertain guests.

KITCHEN — Brightly painted walls contrast with the black cabinetry to grant a stunning and vibrant look to the kitchen.

REAR VIEW — By choosing to add a pool and to screen in the back porch, this homeowner created an impressive and spacious place to enjoy the great outdoors.

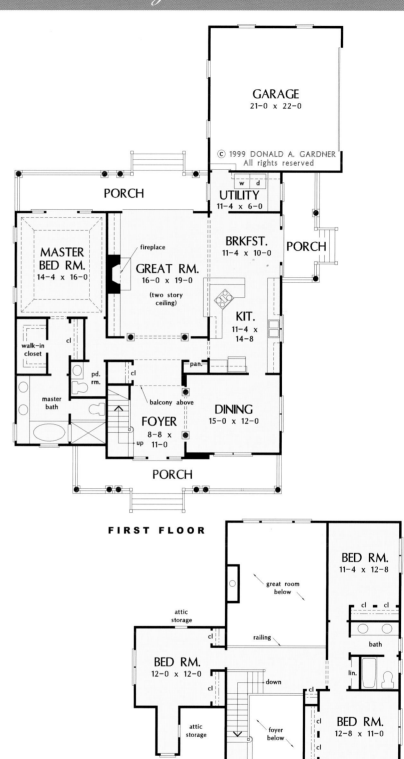

FIRST FLOOR

SECOND FLOOR

TOTAL LIVING	FIRST FLOOR	SECOND FLOOR	BED	BATH	WIDTH	DEPTH	FOUNDATION	PRICE CODE
2500 sq. ft.	1685 sq. ft.	815 sq. ft.	4	2-1/2	52'8"	72'4"	Crawl Space	F

TO ORDER CALL:
1-866-525-9374

PLAN#:
DHDG01-828

Jamestowne

Home photographed may differ from construction documents.

Sater Design Collection
AMERICAN CLASSIC

Chantel

	PLAN#: DHDS01-7011	TO ORDER CALL: 1-866-525-9374

©The Sater Design Collection, Inc.

TOTAL LIVING	FIRST FLOOR	SECOND FLOOR	BED	BATH	WIDTH	DEPTH	FOUNDATION	PRICE CODE
1822 sq. ft.	1822 sq. ft.	N/A	3	2	58'0"	67'2"	Basement	E

The blending of gables, dormers and decorative shutters sets the tone for this intriguing design. A feeling of openness is present with the farm-house's adjoining vaulted living and dining rooms. Triple sliding-glass doors in the living room and master suite open onto the column-lined rear porch. A Palladian window is the home's focal point, providing light to the open living spaces.

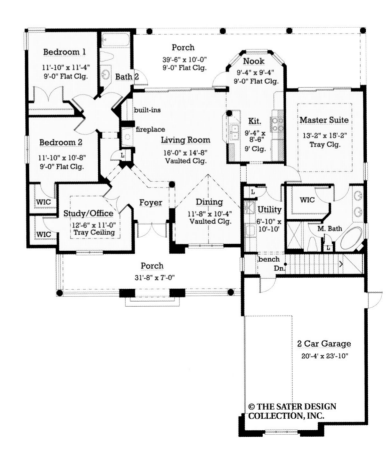

© THE SATER DESIGN COLLECTION, INC.

REAR ELEVATION

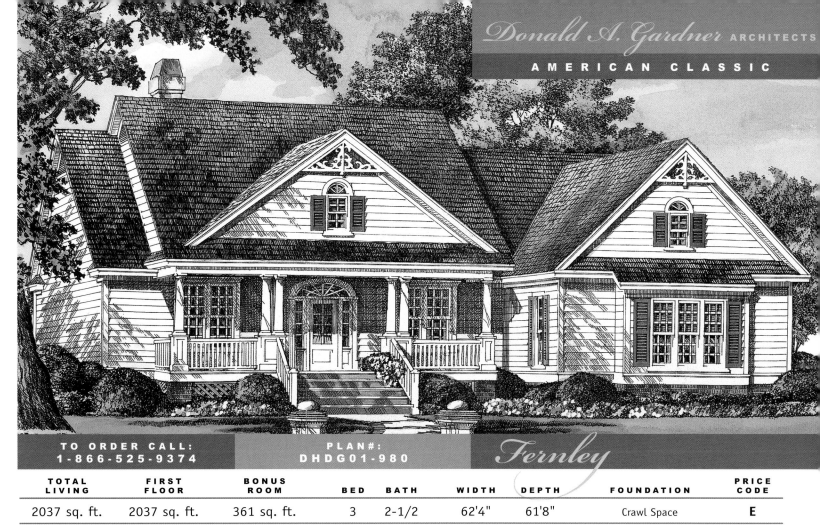

TO ORDER CALL: 1-866-525-9374		**PLAN#:** DHDG01-980					*Fernley*		

TOTAL LIVING	FIRST FLOOR	BONUS ROOM	BED	BATH	WIDTH	DEPTH	FOUNDATION	PRICE CODE
2037 sq. ft.	2037 sq. ft.	361 sq. ft.	3	2-1/2	62'4"	61'8"	Crawl Space	E

©2002 Donald A. Gardner, Inc.

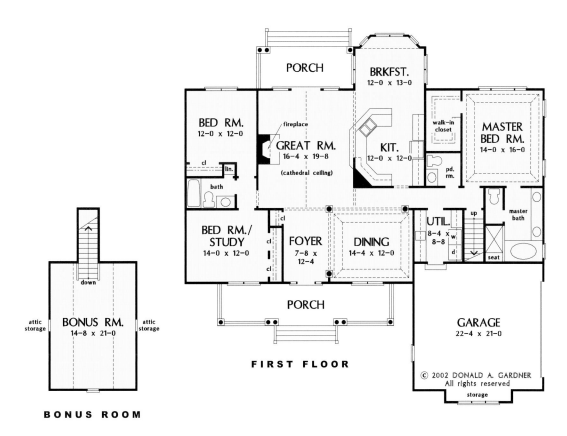

BONUS ROOM

FIRST FLOOR

This traditional starts with columns that provide a shadowbox effect to frame two large windows on the front porch. Inside, an open floor plan creates a natural traffic flow and visual space. A convenient counter separates the kitchen from the gathering rooms, yet allows the cook to keep an eye on children in the great room, backyard and breakfast nook.

REAR ELEVATION

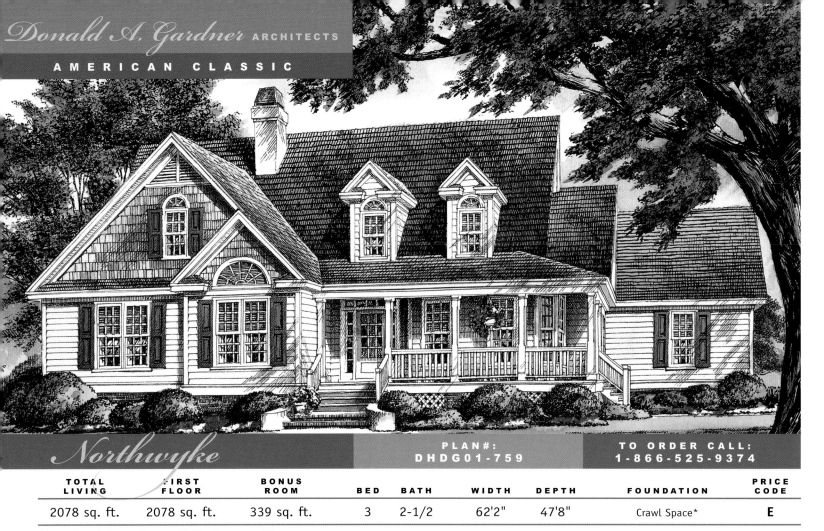

AMERICAN CLASSIC

Northwyke

| | | PLAN#: | | | | | TO ORDER CALL: |

| | | PLAN#: DHDG01-759 | | | | | TO ORDER CALL: 1-866-525-9374 |

TOTAL LIVING	FIRST FLOOR	BONUS ROOM	BED	BATH	WIDTH	DEPTH	FOUNDATION	PRICE CODE
2078 sq. ft.	2078 sq. ft.	339 sq. ft.	3	2-1/2	62'2"	47'8"	Crawl Space*	E

*Other foundation options available. See page 255

Airy bay windows expand both of the home's dining areas, while the great room and kitchen are amplified by a shared cathedral ceiling. The generous great room features a fireplace with flanking built-in cabinetry, skylights and access to a marvelous back porch. A soaring cathedral ceiling enhances the master bedroom, which enjoys a large walk-in closet and private, luxurious bath.

REAR ELEVATION

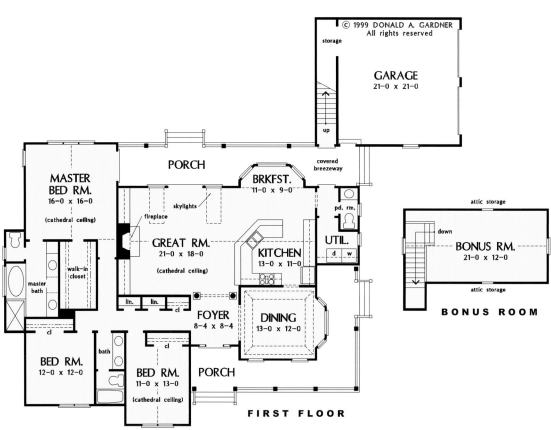

FIRST FLOOR

BONUS ROOM

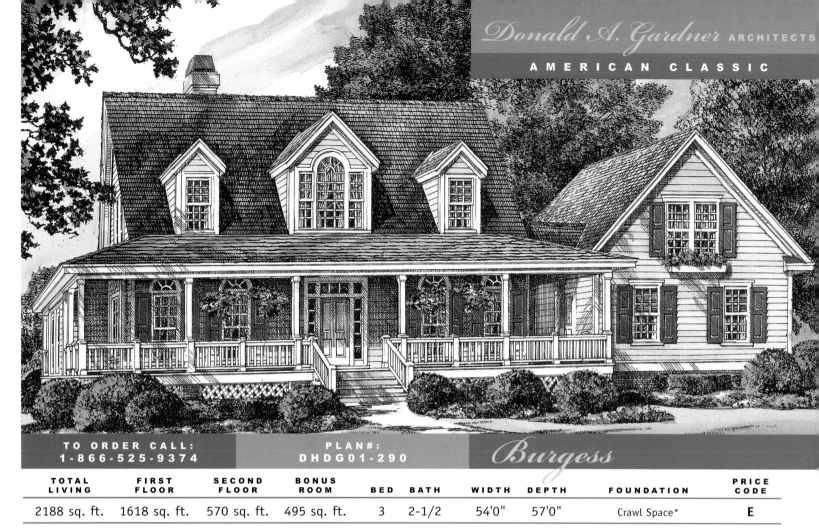

TO ORDER CALL: 1-866-525-9374	PLAN#: DHDG01-290	*Burgess*							

TOTAL LIVING	FIRST FLOOR	SECOND FLOOR	BONUS ROOM	BED	BATH	WIDTH	DEPTH	FOUNDATION	PRICE CODE
2188 sq. ft.	1618 sq. ft.	570 sq. ft.	495 sq. ft.	3	2-1/2	54'0"	57'0"	Crawl Space*	E

©1993 Donald A. Gardner Architects, Inc.

**Other foundation options available. See page 255*

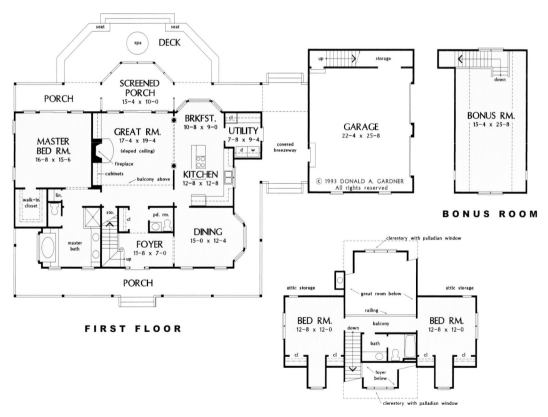

FIRST FLOOR

BONUS ROOM

SECOND FLOOR

A two-story great room and two-story foyer, both with dormer windows, welcome natural light into this graceful country classic with wraparound porch. The large kitchen, featuring a central cooktop island with serving counter and a large breakfast bay, opens to the great room for easy entertaining. Columns punctuate the interior spaces, and the semi-detached garage features a large bonus room.

REAR ELEVATION

Peachtree

PLAN#:	TO ORDER CALL:
DHDG01-524	1-866-525-9374

TOTAL LIVING	FIRST FLOOR	SECOND FLOOR	BONUS ROOM	BED	BATH	WIDTH	DEPTH	FOUNDATION	PRICE CODE
2298 sq. ft.	1743 sq. ft.	555 sq. ft.	350 sq. ft.	4	3	78'0"	53'2"	Crawl Space*	E

*Other foundation options available. See page 255

While the foyer, great room and screened porch enjoy vaulted and cathedral ceilings, spacious nine-foot ceilings are standard throughout the rest of the home. The center dormer with arched window is an asset inside and out, and bay windows perk up the dining room and breakfast area. A downstairs bedroom/study, two upstairs bedrooms and a bonus room provide ample room for growing families.

REAR ELEVATION

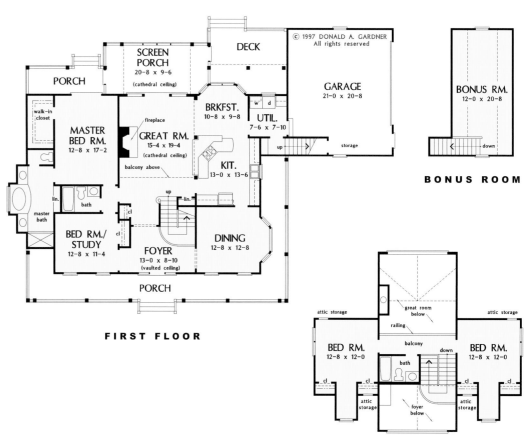

FIRST FLOOR

BONUS ROOM

SECOND FLOOR

| TO ORDER CALL: 1-866-525-9374 | PLAN#: DHFB01-3712 | *Defoors Mill* |

TOTAL LIVING	FIRST FLOOR	SECOND FLOOR	BONUS ROOM	BED	BATH	WIDTH	DEPTH	FOUNDATION	PRICE CODE
2351 sq. ft.	1803 sq. ft.	548 sq. ft.	277 sq. ft.	4	3	55'0"	48'0"	Basement, Crawl Space or Slab	H

©2002 Frank Betz Associates, Inc.

FIRST FLOOR

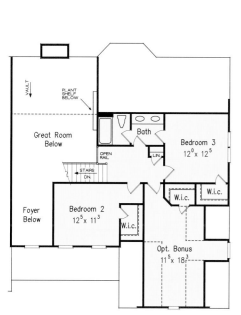

SECOND FLOOR

Tradition is appreciated in the thoughtful design of *Defoors Mill*. The master suite encompasses the entire left wing of the home for comfort and privacy. Special details in this home include a handy island in the kitchen, decorative columns around the dining area and a coat closet just off the garage.

REAR ELEVATION

Donald A. Gardner ARCHITECTS

AMERICAN CLASSIC

Holloway

PLAN#:
DHDG01-1064

TO ORDER CALL:
1-866-525-9374

TOTAL LIVING	FIRST FLOOR	SECOND FLOOR	BONUS ROOM	BED	BATH	WIDTH	DEPTH	FOUNDATION	PRICE CODE
2469 sq. ft.	1977 sq. ft.	492 sq. ft.	374 sq. ft.	4	3	75'1"	44'5"	Crawl Space*	E

*Other foundation options available. See page 255

This impressive brick home features a towering portico, which frames the front door. Formality is achieved by room positioning, yet the floor plan promotes easy living. Two-story ceilings in the foyer and great room help brighten the home by welcoming natural light, while built-in cabinetry flanks the fireplace. Columns punctuate the dining room, and a large bonus room provides versatile space.

REAR ELEVATION

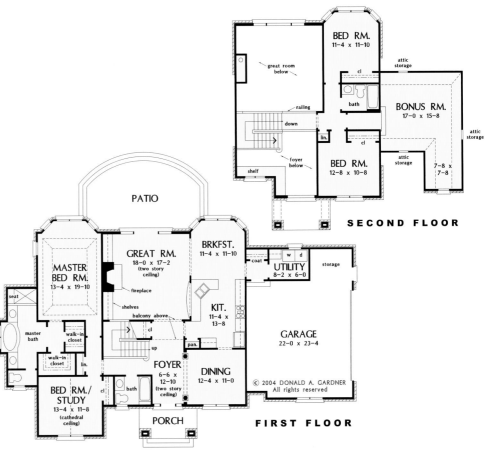

SECOND FLOOR

FIRST FLOOR

TO ORDER CALL: 1-866-525-9374	PLAN#: DHDS01-7005	*Marcella*

TOTAL LIVING	FIRST FLOOR	SECOND FLOOR	BED	BATH	WIDTH	DEPTH	FOUNDATION	PRICE CODE
2487 sq. ft.	2487 sq. ft.	N/A	3	2	70'0"	72'0"	Slab or Opt. Basement	F

©The Sater Design Collection, Inc.

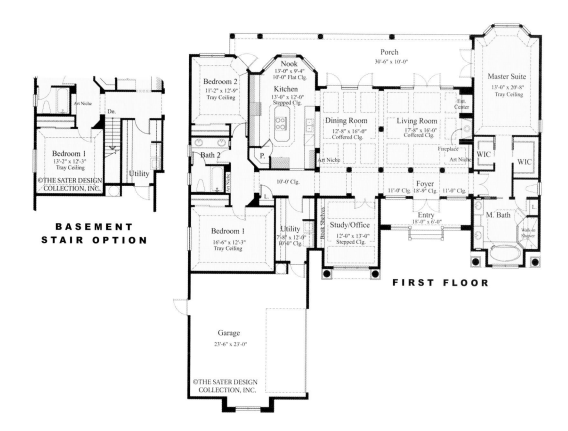

BASEMENT STAIR OPTION

FIRST FLOOR

A striking gable resides over the recessed arch covered entry into this cozy design. Past the foyer, columns and coffered ceilings define the living and dining rooms. A built-in entertainment center, fireplace and art niche add a handcrafted touch to the common living space. Nearby, the kitchen includes a convenient pass-thru to dining room, a walk-in pantry and charming breakfast nook.

REAR ELEVATION

Lunden Valley

PLAN#:
DHDS01-7050

TO ORDER CALL:
1-866-525-9374

TOTAL LIVING	FIRST FLOOR	SECOND FLOOR	BED	BATH	WIDTH	DEPTH	FOUNDATION	PRICE CODE
2555 sq. ft.	2555 sq. ft.	N/A	3	2-1/2	70'6"	76'6"	Crawl Space	G

©The Sater Design Collection, Inc.

This home's charming front porch featuring slumped arches and double columns holds up a large, distinctive front gable. Inside, amenities include beamed, coffered, stepped and tray ceilings, numerous built-ins, a split-floor plan and an abundance of wide, open spaces. The design's connecting great room, island kitchen and nook is a bright and airy gathering spot for friends and family.

REAR ELEVATION

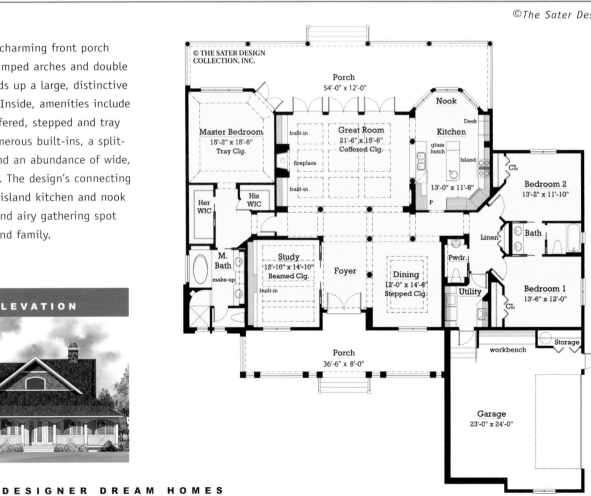

Frank Betz Associates
AMERICAN CLASSIC

TO ORDER CALL: 1-866-525-9374	PLAN#: DHFB01-3551	*Ambrose*

TOTAL LIVING	FIRST FLOOR	SECOND FLOOR	BONUS ROOM	BED	BATH	WIDTH	DEPTH	FOUNDATION	PRICE CODE
2582 sq. ft.	2003 sq. ft.	579 sq. ft.	262 sq. ft.	4	3	54'0"	60'0"	Basement, Crawl Space or Slab	H

©2000 Frank Betz Associates, Inc.

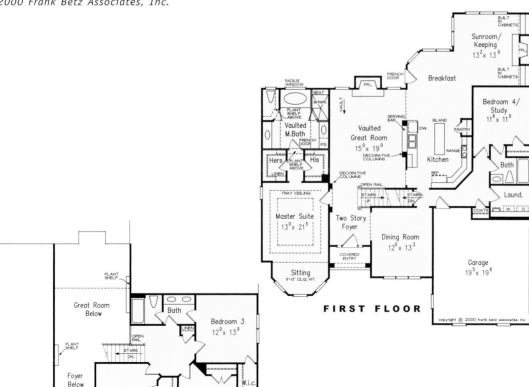

FIRST FLOOR

copyright © 2000 frank betz associates, inc.

A distinctive turret with arched windows is the focal point of the façade on the *Ambrose*. A covered entry leads to an interesting and thoughtful layout inside. Family time is well spent in the large sunroom, situated just beyond the breakfast area. The bedroom on the main level easily transforms into a home office — perfect for the telecommuter or retiree.

SECOND FLOOR

REAR ELEVATION

Donald A. Gardner ARCHITECTS

AMERICAN CLASSIC

Peppermill

PLAN#:
DHDG01-1034

TO ORDER CALL:
1-866-525-9374

TOTAL LIVING	FIRST FLOOR	SECOND FLOOR	BONUS ROOM	BED	BATH	WIDTH	DEPTH	FOUNDATION	PRICE CODE
2586 sq. ft.	1809 sq. ft.	777 sq. ft.	264 sq. ft.	4	3-1/2	70'7"	48'4"	Crawl Space*	F

*Other foundation options available. See page 255

Wrapping a traditional brick exterior with two country porches creates a modern exterior that's big on Southern charm. Bold columns and a metal roof welcome guests inside an equally impressive interior. Both the striking foyer and family room have two-story ceilings, and a tray ceiling tops the master bedroom. The living room/study and bonus room add flexibility for changing needs.

REAR ELEVATION

TO ORDER CALL:
1-866-525-9374

PLAN#:
DHCS01-M2590D2F-0

Greenwood

TOTAL LIVING	FIRST FLOOR	SECOND FLOOR	BED	BATH	WIDTH	DEPTH	FOUNDATION	PRICE CODE
2651 sq. ft.	1190 sq. ft.	1461 sq. ft.	4	2-1/2	42'0"	42'0"	Crawl Space	F

©CornerStone Designs, LLC

SECOND FLOOR

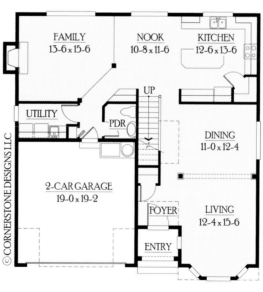

FIRST FLOOR

Classic details distinguish this amazingly compact and versatile home. The dramatic exterior is accented with shingles, arches, oval and bay windows, while the floor plan flows easily through spacious formal and family living spaces. The spacious master suite is segregated from the children for welcome privacy, while the generous bonus room is a perfect spot for TV and games.

REAR ELEVATION

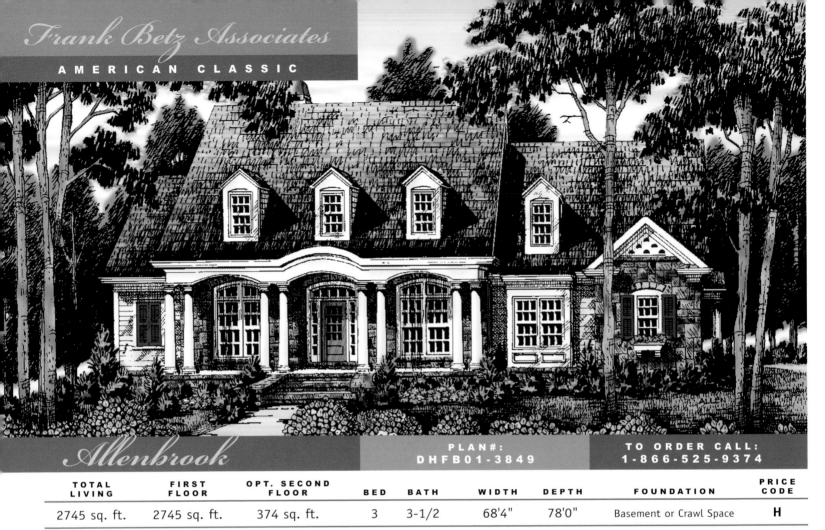

Frank Betz Associates

AMERICAN CLASSIC

Allenbrook

	PLAN#:	TO ORDER CALL:
	DHFB01-3849	1-866-525-9374

TOTAL LIVING	FIRST FLOOR	OPT. SECOND FLOOR	BED	BATH	WIDTH	DEPTH	FOUNDATION	PRICE CODE
2745 sq. ft.	2745 sq. ft.	374 sq. ft.	3	3-1/2	68'4"	78'0"	Basement or Crawl Space	H

©2003 Frank Betz Associates, Inc.

Cheery dormers and a covered front porch give the *Allenbrook* a friendly, time-tested curb appeal. A fireplace lights the cozy keeping room that adjoins the kitchen area. The vaulted family room has an impressive wall of built-in cabinetry and another fireplace. Its split-bedroom design adds an aspect of privacy to the master suite.

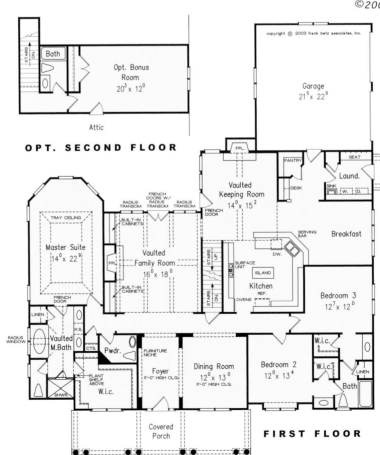

OPT. SECOND FLOOR

FIRST FLOOR

REAR ELEVATION

TO ORDER CALL: 1-866-525-9374	PLAN#: DHFB01-3846	*Wilson Bridge*

TOTAL LIVING	FIRST FLOOR	OPT. SECOND FLOOR	BED	BATH	WIDTH	DEPTH	FOUNDATION	PRICE CODE
2753 sq. ft.	2753 sq. ft.	504 sq. ft.	4	3-1/2	63'0"	68'6"	Basement, Crawl Space or Slab	I

©2003 Frank Betz Associates, Inc.

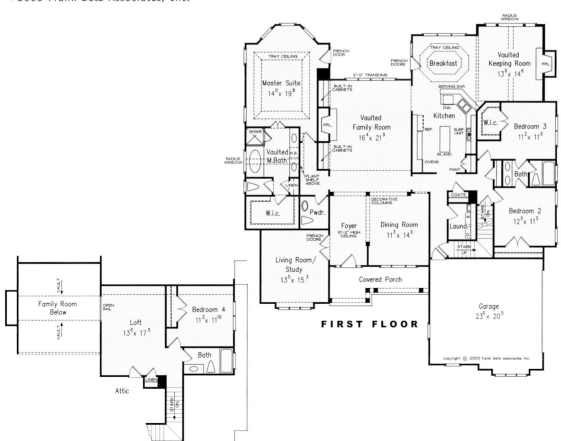

FIRST FLOOR

OPT. SECOND FLOOR

The *Wilson Bridge* has many of the special details that make a house a home. Decorative columns are used to define the border between the foyer and dining room. A vaulted ceiling and fireplace make the keeping room a casual and cozy extension of the kitchen. Built-in cabinetry adds character to the family room, not to mention additional storage.

REAR ELEVATION

CornerStone Designs
AMERICAN CLASSIC

Chinook

	PLAN#: DHCS01-M2770A3S-0				TO ORDER CALL: 1-866-525-9374			

TOTAL LIVING	FIRST FLOOR	SECOND FLOOR	BED	BATH	WIDTH	DEPTH	FOUNDATION	PRICE CODE
2770 sq. ft.	1510 sq. ft.	1260 sq. ft.	4	2-1/2	72'0"	62'0"	Crawl Space	F

©CornerStone Designs, LLC

Sweeping vistas of the great out-doors are captured from the grand wraparound porches of the *Chinook*. Its Lodge-Craftsman styling, set off by stone and shingles, conveys a sense of rustic elegance. The open floor plan flows around the dramatic, angled central stair, with the soaring entry foyer incorporating an overlook study loft. The master suite's sitting room and private balcony create a luxurious refuge.

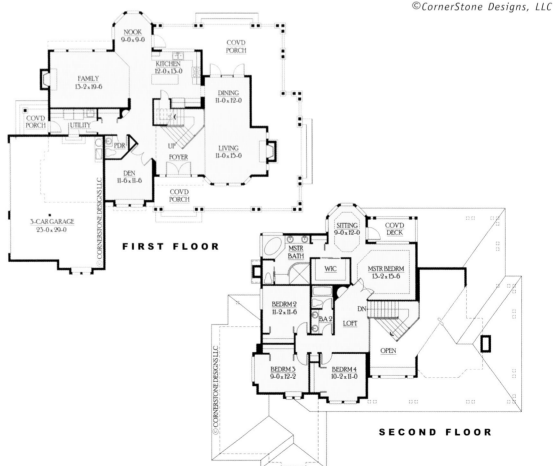

FIRST FLOOR

SECOND FLOOR

REAR ELEVATION

TO ORDER CALL: 1-866-525-9374	PLAN#: DHDS01-7023	*Ansel Arbor*

TOTAL LIVING	FIRST FLOOR	SECOND FLOOR	BONUS ROOM	BED	BATH	WIDTH	DEPTH	FOUNDATION	PRICE CODE
2889 sq. ft.	2151 sq. ft.	738 sq. ft.	534 sq. ft.	3	2-1/2	99'0"	56'0"	Crawl Space or Opt. Basement	G

©*The Sater Design Collection, Inc.*

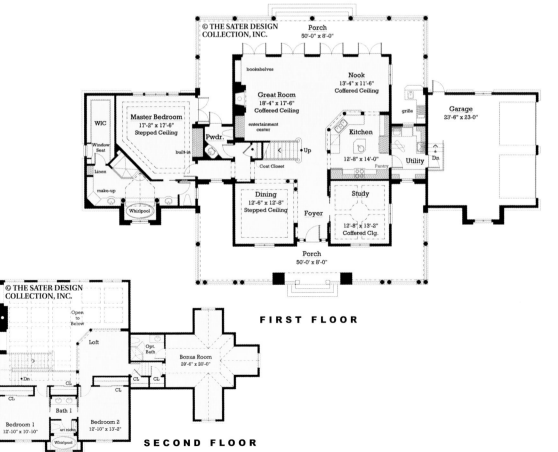

FIRST FLOOR

SECOND FLOOR

Mirrored front and rear wraparound porches are as inviting as the open-floor plan inside. Straight through the foyer, the spacious great room features a coffered ceiling, built-in cabinets, entertainment center, fireplace and French doors to the back porch. Two-story columns rise from the kitchen pass-thru to the loft. A spacious pantry, center work island and an eating bar enhance the kitchen.

REAR ELEVATION

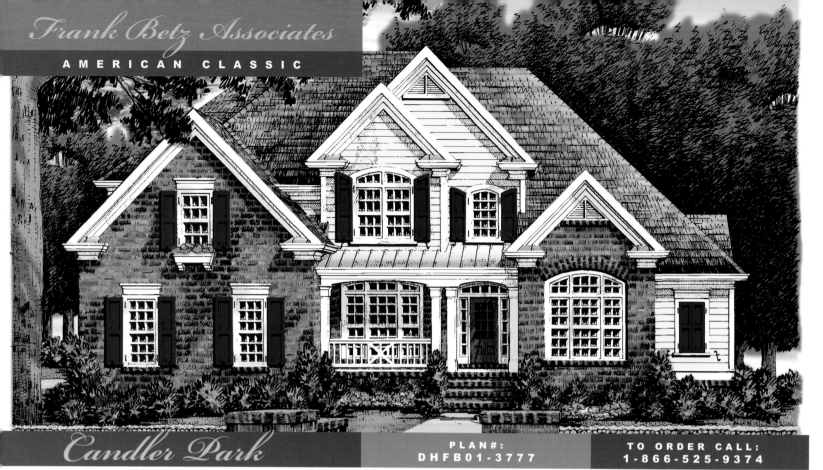

Candler Park

PLAN#:	TO ORDER CALL:
DHFB01-3777	1-866-525-9374

TOTAL LIVING	FIRST FLOOR	SECOND FLOOR	BONUS ROOM	BED	BATH	WIDTH	DEPTH	FOUNDATION	PRICE CODE
2900 sq. ft.	2262 sq. ft.	638 sq. ft.	252 sq. ft.	4	4	64'0"	56'4"	Basement, Crawl Space or Slab	I

©2003 Frank Betz Associates, Inc.

A covered front porch gives a warm welcome to guests as they enter the *Candler Park*. A two-story foyer extends the friendly greeting. A vaulted keeping room — with a fireplace as its backdrop — provides a cozy spot to visit. An optional bonus room is available upstairs, making the perfect playroom, exercise area or home office.

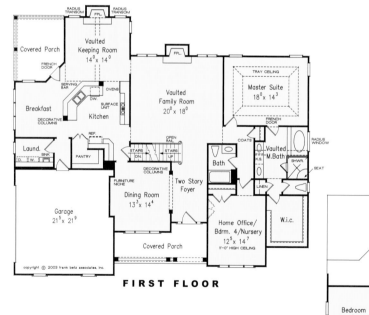

FIRST FLOOR

REAR ELEVATION

SECOND FLOOR

TO ORDER CALL: 1-866-525-9374	PLAN#: DHFB01-3598	*Ashton*

TOTAL LIVING	FIRST FLOOR	SECOND FLOOR	BONUS ROOM	BED	BATH	WIDTH	DEPTH	FOUNDATION	PRICE CODE
3024 sq. ft.	2146 sq. ft.	878 sq. ft.	341 sq. ft.	4	3-1/2	61'0"	60'4"	Basement, Crawl Space or Slab	I

©2001 Frank Betz Associates, Inc.

SECOND FLOOR

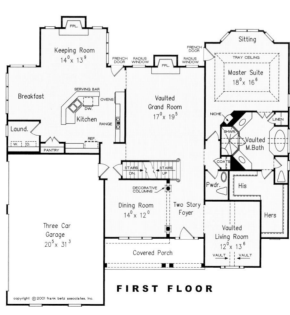

FIRST FLOOR

Traditional on the outside and innovative on the inside, the *Ashton* incorporates the best of both worlds! A keeping room connects to the kitchen area, providing the perfect place for relaxing family time. The master suite is truly luxurious with a bayed sitting area, his-and-her closets and a decorative art niche.

REAR ELEVATION

Clarkson

	PLAN#:						TO ORDER CALL:	
	DHDG01-1117						1-866-525-9374	

TOTAL LIVING	FIRST FLOOR	BONUS ROOM	BED	BATH	WIDTH	DEPTH	FOUNDATION	PRICE CODE
3080 sq. ft.	3080 sq. ft.	498 sq. ft.	4	4-1/2	75'7"	72'3"	Crawl Space*	G

*Other foundation options available. See page 255

For families that want a large square-footage with the convenience of one floor, this home encompasses all that is luxury, one-story living. With a sprawling master suite and completely open kitchen, breakfast and morning room combination, large living spaces are abounding. The massive utility area provides room for more than just washing clothes, while the screened porch with cathedral ceiling is a nice architectural detail.

REAR ELEVATION

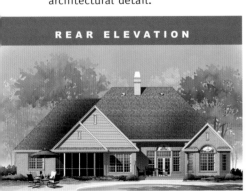

FIRST FLOOR

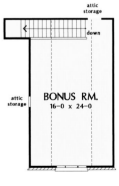

BONUS ROOM

TO ORDER CALL: 1-866-525-9374	PLAN#: DHDG01-452	*Arbordale*

TOTAL LIVING	FIRST FLOOR	SECOND FLOOR	BONUS ROOM	BED	BATH	WIDTH	DEPTH	FOUNDATION	PRICE CODE
3163 sq. ft.	2086 sq. ft.	1077 sq. ft.	403 sq. ft.	4	3-1/2	82'10"	51'8"	Crawl Space*	G

©1996 Donald A. Gardner Architects, Inc.

Home photographed may differ from construction documents.

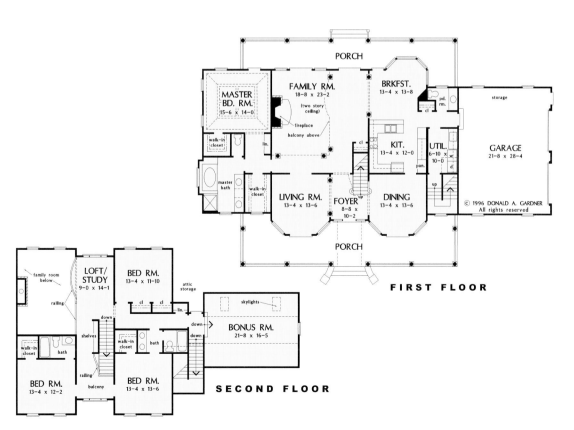

FIRST FLOOR

SECOND FLOOR

This beautiful farmhouse with twin gables and bays adds just the right amount of country style to modern family life. The master suite is tucked away downstairs with no bedrooms directly above, and the cook of the family will love the spacious kitchen with ample cabinets and pantry. Storage space abounds with walk-ins, hall shelves and a linen closet upstairs.

REAR VIEW

Monroe

TOTAL LIVING	FIRST FLOOR	SECOND FLOOR	BED	BATH	WIDTH	DEPTH	FOUNDATION	PRICE CODE
3166 sq. ft.	2175 sq. ft.	991 sq. ft.	4	3-1/2	62'0"	78'8"	Slab	K

Home photographed may differ from construction documents.

©*Garrell Associates, Inc.*

Historic precedent is followed in the exterior of the *Monroe*. However, the plan has been modernized for today's family. The large foyer invites you into the family and dining rooms. From there the master suite on the main floor offers one-level convenience. This open floor plan is great for entertaining or a cozy evening with the family.

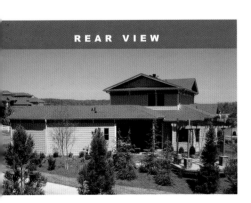

REAR VIEW

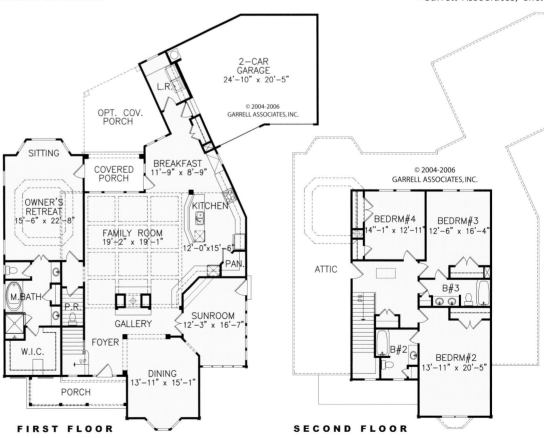

FIRST FLOOR

SECOND FLOOR

TO ORDER CALL: 1-866-525-9374	PLAN#: DHFB01-3656	Laurel River

TOTAL LIVING	FIRST FLOOR	OPT. SECOND FLOOR	BED	BATH	WIDTH	DEPTH	FOUNDATION	PRICE CODE
3190 sq. ft.	3190 sq. ft.	305 sq. ft.	5	4-1/2	74'0"	84'6"	Basement, Crawl Space or Slab	I

©2001 Frank Betz Associates, Inc.

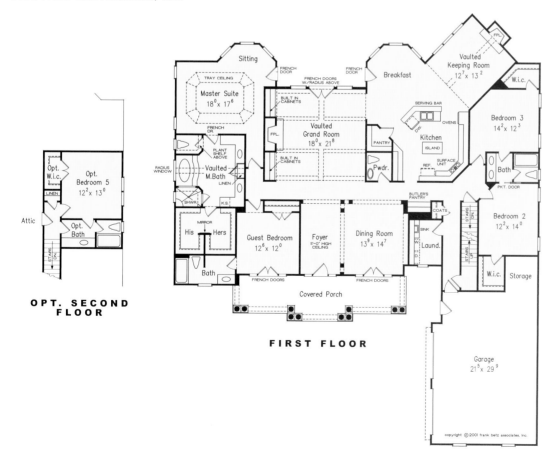

OPT. SECOND FLOOR

FIRST FLOOR

What was old is new again, and its come back even better than before. A vaulted grand room commands attention as you enter the home. It leads to a comfortable collaboration of a kitchen, breakfast and keeping room. A butler's pantry is situated between the kitchen and dining room, making it convenient to host gatherings.

REAR ELEVATION

Candelaria

	PLAN#:	TO ORDER CALL:
	DHGA01-00219	1-866-525-9374

TOTAL LIVING	FIRST FLOOR	SECOND FLOOR	BED	BATH	WIDTH	DEPTH	FOUNDATION	PRICE CODE
3237 sq. ft.	2450 sq. ft.	787 sq. ft.	4	3-1/2	68'11"	65'7"	Basement or Crawl Space	H

Home photographed may differ from construction documents.

©*Garrell Associates, Inc.*

This unique first-floor layout features dramatic spaces and intimate areas that give the home an "air of excitement" and a feeling of warmth. The master suite offers a retreat for the owner with its sitting area and luxurious bath. Designed for the move-up homeowner, this plan incorporates features that are typically seen in much larger homes.

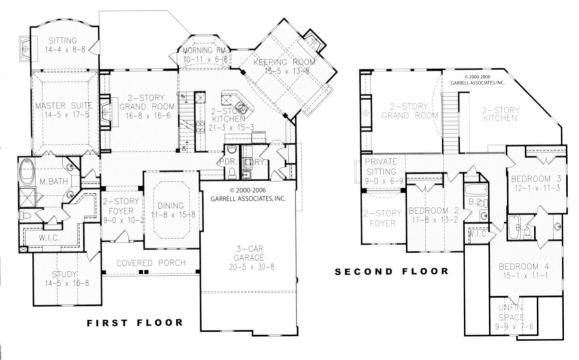

FIRST FLOOR

SECOND FLOOR

REAR VIEW

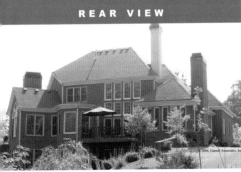

TO ORDER CALL: 1-866-525-9374	PLAN#: DHFB01-3942	*Ansley Cottage*

TOTAL LIVING	FIRST FLOOR	SECOND FLOOR	BONUS ROOM	BED	BATH	WIDTH	DEPTH	FOUNDATION	PRICE CODE
3295 sq. ft.	1744 sq. ft.	1551 sq. ft.	443 sq. ft.	4	4	47'4"	79'4"	Basement, Crawl Space or Slab	I

©2005 Frank Betz Associates, Inc.

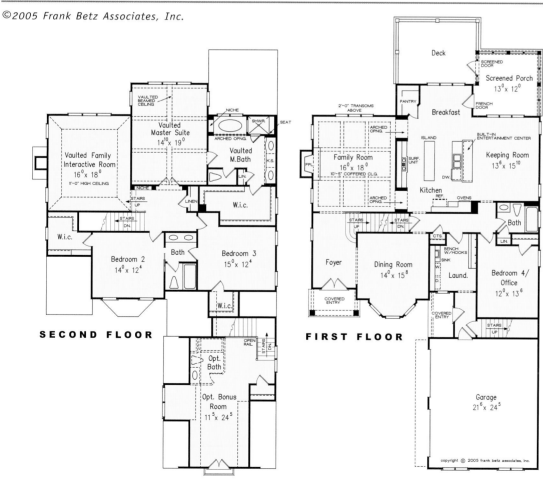

SECOND FLOOR

FIRST FLOOR

The *Ansley Cottage* offers the amenities that so many homeowners are searching for today. The lower level has a bedroom with a full bathroom, perfect for guests or as a home office. The keeping room is a great place to spend time with family and friends. The upper level has the master suite and two bedrooms that share a Jack-and-Jill bathroom and walk-in closets. An interactive family room can be used as a media room, playroom or exercise room.

REAR ELEVATION

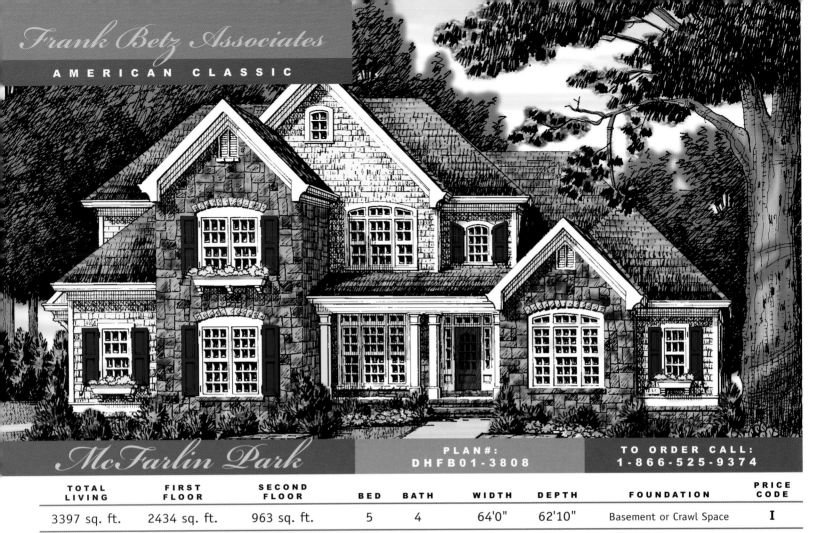

McFarlin Park

	PLAN#: DHFB01-3808		TO ORDER CALL: 1-866-525-9374

TOTAL LIVING	FIRST FLOOR	SECOND FLOOR	BED	BATH	WIDTH	DEPTH	FOUNDATION	PRICE CODE
3397 sq. ft.	2434 sq. ft.	963 sq. ft.	5	4	64'0"	62'10"	Basement or Crawl Space	I

From the Southern Living® Design Collection — The timeless façade of the *McFarlin Park* is a welcoming blend of stone and cedar shake. Inside, a vaulted keeping room adjoins the kitchen area, creating the perfect spot for lounging or entertaining guests. Unwind on the cozy screened porch, tucked away off the kitchen. A loft overlooks the family room — perfect for a computer desk or sitting area.

REAR ELEVATION

FIRST FLOOR

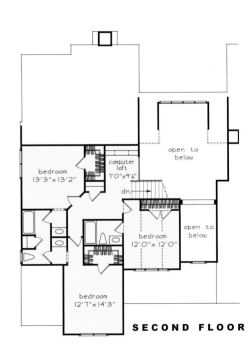

SECOND FLOOR

TO ORDER CALL: 1-866-525-9374	PLAN#: DHGA01-05207	*Brookmoore*

TOTAL LIVING	FIRST FLOOR	SECOND FLOOR	BED	BATH	WIDTH	DEPTH	FOUNDATION	PRICE CODE
3475 sq. ft.	2491 sq. ft.	984 sq. ft.	4	4-1/2	70'9"	68'5"	Basement	H

©Garrell Associates, Inc.

Home photographed may differ from construction documents.

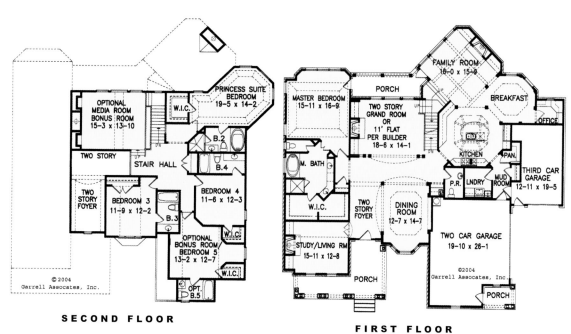

SECOND FLOOR

FIRST FLOOR

Brick, stone and shingle make up the exterior of this modern plan. A reverse-angled family room adds interest to the kitchen and breakfast rooms. The master suite features a private bath, generous walk-in closet and views to the backyard. The upper level consists of three additional bedrooms, an optional media room and fifth bedroom.

REAR ELEVATION

Seaoria

PLAN#:	TO ORDER CALL:
DHCS01-M4060A3F-5	1-866-525-9374

TOTAL LIVING	FIRST FLOOR	SECOND FLOOR	BED	BATH	WIDTH	DEPTH	FOUNDATION	PRICE CODE
4160 sq. ft.	2000 sq. ft.	2160 sq. ft.	4	3-1/2	65'0"	79'6"	Crawl Space	K

©CornerStone Designs, LLC

A vision of Victorian elegance greets you, highlighted by the signature corner turret. From the columned wraparound entry porch to the traditional foyer accessing the formal rooms, a bold diagonal axis draws you through the dramatic two-story octagonal rotunda into the grand family room. Full of romance and packed with detail, the *Seaoria* is a grand modern expression of old-fashioned family living.

FIRST FLOOR

SECOND FLOOR

REAR VIEW

TO ORDER CALL:
1-866-525-9374

PLAN#:
DHCS01-M4100A3F-0

Cedar Ridge

TOTAL LIVING	FIRST FLOOR	SECOND FLOOR	BED	BATH	WIDTH	DEPTH	FOUNDATION	PRICE CODE
4220 sq. ft.	2075 sq. ft.	2145 sq. ft.	4	3-1/2	90'0"	60'0"	Crawl Space	H

©CornerStone Designs, LLC

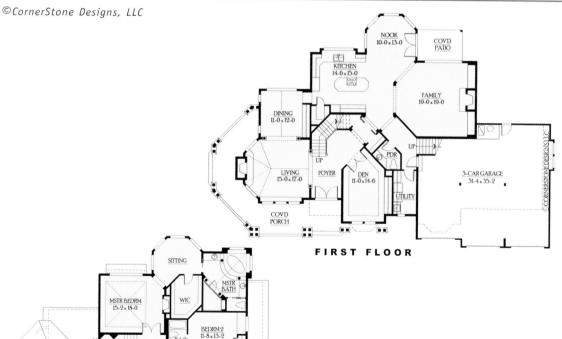

FIRST FLOOR

SECOND FLOOR

This grand Craftsman estate creates a feeling of elegance while providing every modern convenience. The floor plan marries vaulted formal rooms and open family spaces to the outdoors with generous front and rear covered porches. A grand front stair leads to the luxurious master suite, while the private back stair accesses the bonus room and three secondary bedrooms.

REAR VIEW

Vacation Collection

Amicalola Cottage - **FRONT EXTERIOR**
& REAR DECK
GARRELL ASSOCIATES - See page 202

Santa Rosa - **LIVING ROOM**
SATER DESIGN COLLECTION - See page 216

VACATION / WATERFRONT / MOUNTAIN

These are the homes where memories are made and kept forever —

the classic homes that form the reason why people long

to be on vacation. Their massive, wraparound porches are made for

leisurely afternoons with books, games and family. Their generous great rooms and

large, open kitchens are designed for gathering, for fun and entertainment.

Their spacious, open floor plans encourage interaction, movement and the joy of

being "home away from home". And their large bedrooms,

private master suites, secluded balconies and inviting fireplaces have been

created for solitude, for romance — for long days and cool, comfortable nights.

More than merely vacations, these homes offer enjoyment, respite and

a welcome state of mind that endures.

Santa Rosa -
SATER DESIGN COLLECTION - See page 216

Aruba Bay

© THE SATER DESIGN COLLECTION, INC.

PLAN# DHDS01-6840   **1-866-525-9374**

Creative room placement in an unrestricted floor plan makes this the perfect vacation home. An elevated balcony entryway and varied rooflines greet those who pass by. Multiple porches, a leisure room with fireplace, and upper-level bedrooms with a deck create a thoughtful, open floor plan that invites fresh breezes, wide views and good friends.

Entertaining is a breeze in the dining room, just steps from the kitchen and great room. An oversized window and glass door to one of the main level's three porches connect the space with the outdoors.

Another spot for entertaining is the optional billiard room on the lower level. A full wet bar, sliding doors and white-trimmed windows give the space its custom feel. As you can see, the home invites fun, relaxation and memory making.

KITCHEN — The kitchen offers lots of serving space with its deep, curved counter and long wall of cabinetry culminating in a corner pantry. Open to the dining and great rooms, it's the home's center stage.

GREAT ROOM — French doors lead from the great room to the front porch, where quiet evenings are spent. Reflected in the mirror is a balcony loft.

DINING ROOM — A large, airy dining room is just steps from the kitchen and great room. A French door to one of the main level's three porches connects the space with the outdoors.

GREAT ROOM — Packed with functional and aesthetic details like a smart great room/dining room/kitchen design to large, sunny decks, the home invites fun and relaxation. The marble surround and classic mantle create an easy focal point for the leisure room, while arched transom windows heighten views.

REAR VIEW — Large, layered decks make it clear that this home is made for relaxing — with good friends, good books, or a good cup of coffee.

MASTER BATH — An elegant garden tub commands relaxation in the master bath, where a large window embraces each day's sunrise and sunset.

MASTER BEDROOM — The master suite is secluded to one side of the first floor and boasts an oversized bedroom with a private porch.

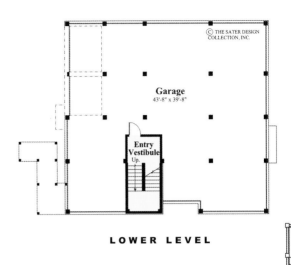

Garage
43'-8" x 39'-8"

Entry Vestibule
Up.

© THE SATER DESIGN COLLECTION, INC.

LOWER LEVEL

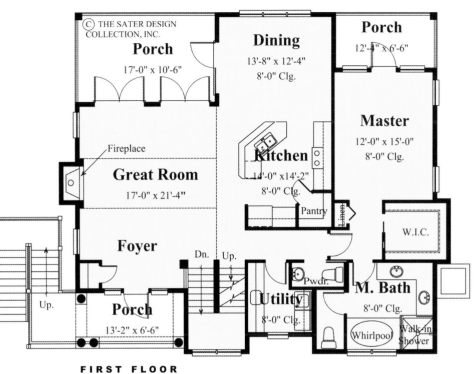

© THE SATER DESIGN COLLECTION, INC.

Porch
17'-0" x 10'-6"

Dining
13'-8" x 12'-4"
8'-0" Clg.

Porch
12'-4" x 6'-6"

Fireplace

Great Room
17'-0" x 21'-4"

Kitchen
14'-0" x14'-2"
8'-0" Clg.

Master
12'-0" x 15'-0"
8'-0" Clg.

Pantry

W.I.C.

Foyer

Dn. Up.

Up.

Porch
13'-2" x 6'-6"

Pwdr.

Utility
8'-0" Clg.

M. Bath
8'-0" Clg.

Whirlpool

Walk-in Shower

FIRST FLOOR

BASEMENT — A full wet bar, sliding doors and white-trimmed windows give the finished basement its custom feel.

© THE SATER DESIGN COLLECTION, INC.

Open Deck
17'-0" x 10'-6"

Bedroom
13'-8" x 12'-0"
12'-0" Clg.

W.I.C.

Tub

Open to Below
23'-0" Clg.

Loft
8'-0" Clg.

Bath 2

Linen

Dn. Up.

Bedroom
10'-0" x 13'-2"
12'-0" Clg.

Closet

SECOND FLOOR

| TO ORDER CALL: 1-866-525-9374 | PLAN#: DHDS01-6840 | *Aruba Bay* |

TOTAL LIVING	FIRST FLOOR	SECOND FLOOR	LOWER LEVEL	BED	BATH	WIDTH	DEPTH	FOUNDATION	PRICE CODE
1886 sq. ft.	1342 sq. ft.	511 sq. ft.	33 sq. ft.	3	2-1/2	44'0"	40'0"	Island Basement	G

Home photographed may differ from construction documents.

Riva Ridge

© 2005 ALLORA, LLC

PLAN# DHAL01-5013   1-866-525-9374

Nature's flair embraces this rural cottage. For those whose idea of vacation is enjoying a quiet weekend in the mountains in a rustic but contemporary home, the *Riva Ridge* is for you! A stylish blend of cottage living and lavish architectural detail, the *Riva Ridge* embraces the outdoors in a comfortable and modern floor plan. An exciting ensemble of siding and stone, copper roofing and detached garage gives this Craftsman home irresistible curb appeal. For days when weather doesn't cooperate, the basement level houses the ideal media room or child's playroom. Featuring two bedrooms, the downstairs also boasts a large rec room and outdoor covered patio that perfectly melds indoor with outdoor living. For those who love all things natural, the *Riva Ridge* is a perfect fit!

KITCHEN/DINING — With easy access to the dining and great rooms, entertaining in the kitchen is a breeze.

DINING ROOM — Surrounded by windows and accessing the screen porch, the dining room rests in a box-bay window that provides panoramic scenery at every meal.

GREAT ROOM — The vaulted ceiling adds vertical volume, while a stone fireplace showcases elegant architectural detail.

MASTER BATH — Truly luxurious, the master bathroom includes his-and-her sinks and a private toilet. The separate shower and bathtub not only promote convenience, but also add elegance to the master bath.

GREAT ROOM — Designed for entertaining, the great room features a rear wall of windows that bathe the room with sunlight for widespread illumination. Naturally flowing into the dining room and kitchen, the great room also accesses the deck.

MASTER BEDROOM — Accessing a private rear deck, the master bedroom is positioned for privacy. A spacious walk-in closet grants luxury, while a cathedral ceiling increases vertical volume.

REAR VIEW — Screen porches, decks and a box-bay window add interest and combine with stone columns and several windows for an attractive rear exterior.

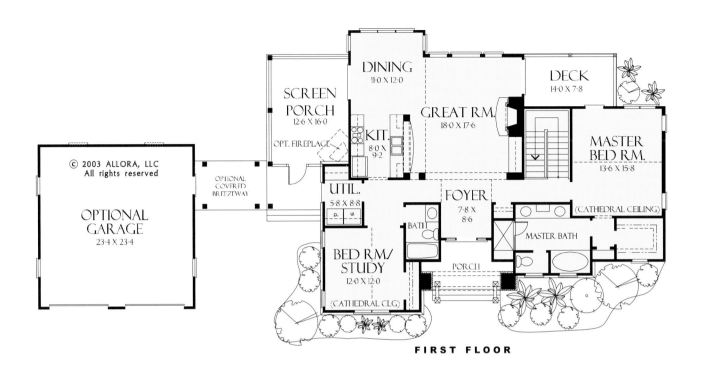

FIRST FLOOR

PORCH/DECK — When enjoying alfresco meals, the rear deck is the perfect place to entertain many or appreciate privacy. Facing the backyard, both the deck and screen porch with optional fireplace provide ample space to take in scenic views.

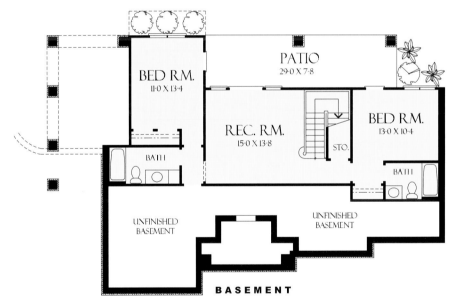

BASEMENT

TO ORDER CALL: 1-866-525-9374		PLAN#: DHAL01-5013		*Riva Ridge*					
TOTAL LIVING	**FIRST FLOOR**	**BASEMENT**	**BED**	**BATH**	**WIDTH**	**DEPTH**	**FOUNDATION**		**PRICE CODE**
2263 sq. ft.	1428 sq. ft.	835 sq. ft.	4	4	60'6"	41'7"	Hillside Walkout		0

Home photographed may differ from construction documents.

© GARRELL ASSOCIATES, INC.

PLAN# DHGA01-05168   1-866-525-9374

The *Amicalola Cottage* promotes open living spaces with a floor plan that provides abundant places to enjoy calming views, elegantly blending the outdoors with the indoors. From covered porches and multiple decks to a large lodge room, this home embraces tranquil living.

Before you walk through the front door, take a minute to appreciate the beauty of the natural-looking exterior. A truly remarkable façade, this home features ornately carved gable peaks, a sprawling rooftop with various pitches and a decorative single dormer. The covered porch provides a dry place to enjoy Mother Nature, while dramatic wooden columns punctuate the exterior.

Upon entry into the home, a barrel-vaulted foyer and adjacent dining room immediately greet guests. With a built-in fireplace and vaulted ceiling, the lodge room features a wall of windows and boasts grandeur all around.

DINING ROOM — Natural light enters from three sides of this unique dining room. Accented with stacked stone and wood columns, this open room is perfect for casual as well as elegant dining.

KITCHEN — Arched stacked stone on the exhaust chimney gives an open feeling of a window where one does not exist. A beautiful feast of colors and textures are created by the cabinets, walls and ceiling treatments of this gourmet kitchen.

LODGE ROOM — The giant arched wall of windows provides a stunning way to enjoy rear views and natural sunlight.

COVERED PORCH/DECK — Step out and enjoy tranquil living at its finest. Outdoor living takes on a new meaning with this rear patio that gives you grand views both inside and out.

COVERED PORCH — A main-level covered porch features a fireplace and grilling area as well as opens to a spacious deck for outdoor relaxation and entertaining.

FRONT PORCH — Take a walk to this beckoning front porch to sit a moment and take in the great outdoors. Then make your way to this grand entry that leads to an extraordinary home.

OPTIONAL SECOND FLOOR — This additional private living space offers diverse flexibility. It is perfect for teens or in-laws as well as guests or a home office.

MASTER BATH — The center bathtub with generous separate shower gives this master bathroom a truly spacious feel.

OPTIONAL SECOND FLOOR

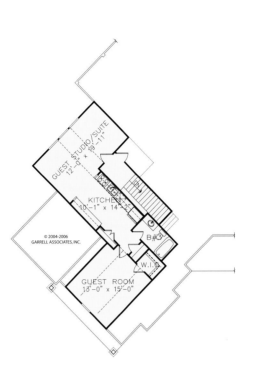

GUEST STUDIO/SUITE 12'-0" x 19'-11"
KITCHEN 10'-1" x 14'-2"
B#3
GUEST ROOM 13'-0" x 15'-0"
W.I.C.
© 2004-2006 GARRELL ASSOCIATES, INC.

FIRST FLOOR

COVERED PORCH
OPEN DECK
© 2004-2006 GARRELL ASSOCIATES, INC.
BRKFST 12'-5" x 16'-11"
SCREENED PORCH 16'-5" x 15'-2"
COVERED ROOF
MASTER SUITE 18'-11" x 16'-6"
W.I.C.
DECK
BEDROOM #3 14'-9" x 14'-7"
KITCHEN 25'-2" x 8'-6"
LODGE ROOM 20'-3" x 17'-9"
W.I.C.
B#2
LAUNDRY 7'-10" x 8'-7"
M. BATH
BEDROOM #2 14'-8" x 14'-1"
MUD ROOM 8'-7" x 8'-4"
DINING 11'-11" x 14'-0"
STUDY 10'-7" x 12'-0"
P.R.
FOYER
2 CAR GARAGE 20'-4" x 24'-11"
COVERED PORCH

OPTIONAL TERRACE

SPA
COVERED PATIO
FUTURE BAR
COVERED PATIO
FUTURE CARD ROOM 18'-6" x 15'-3"
FUTURE SOCIAL ROOM 17'-8" x 17'-11"
FUTURE BEDROOM #4 18'-1 x 13'-6
UNFINISHED ROOM 19'-8 x 13'-8
W.I.C.
W.I.C.
FUTURE B#4
FUTURE B#5
P.R.
VESTIBULE
FUTURE THEATER 19'-10 x 12'-8
STORAGE 10'-7 x 12'-8
FUTURE BEDROOM#5 13'-9 x 14'-4
STORAGE 14'-7 x 13'-8
© 2004-2006 GARRELL ASSOCIATES, INC.

REAR ELEVATION — The curved outdoor living space of this unique design maximizes panoramic views to the rear of this home.

Additional versions available: the Harmony Mountain Cottage, the Lakeview Cottage (smaller) and the Tranquility (larger).

TO ORDER CALL: 1-866-525-9374	PLAN#: DHGA01-05168	*Amicalola Cottage*

TOTAL LIVING	FIRST FLOOR	OPT. TERRACE	OPT. SECOND FLOOR	BED	BATH	WIDTH	DEPTH	FOUNDATION	PRICE CODE
3126 sq. ft.	3126 sq. ft.	3058 sq. ft.	732 sq. ft.	3	2-1/2	103'8"	83'2"	Slab or Basement	0

Home photographed may differ from construction documents.

©*Garrell Associates, Inc.*

Adelaide

© 2000 DONALD A. GARDNER ARCHITECTS

PLAN# DHDG01-866-D   **1-866-525-9374**

Charming yet refined, the *Adelaide* is a classic combination of Craftsman home and an impressive, spacious floor plan. Twin dormers and cedar shake siding add curb appeal to this design, while the two decks, screened porch and generous patio provide space for countless hours to enjoy Mother Nature.

The large master suite features an adjacent private deck, while dual walk-in closets and the large bathroom simplify morning rituals. Located in the rear of the home, the master bedroom provides the utmost privacy. From decorative ceilings and columns, to fireplaces and a shower seat, niceties are abundant.

A bedroom/study with walk-in closet and adjacent full bath can function as a guest suite. The basement's two additional bedrooms and large rec room overlook a covered patio. As the ideal vacation home, the *Adelaide* features your favorite amenities within a modern floor plan.

DINING ROOM — In the formal dining room, an elegant tray ceiling and columns that define the room's perimeter showcase architectural detail. An arched transom highlights three windows to enable a sneak peek at Mother Nature when enjoying meals.

BASEMENT REC ROOM — Built-in shelves and a wet bar bring refreshment and convenience one-step closer, while multiple sets of French doors provide stimulating scenery.

GREAT ROOM — Exposed wooden beams and a cathedral ceiling enhance the lofty great room, while the stone fireplace serves as the stunning focal point.

GREAT ROOM — Completely open to the kitchen and breakfast room, the great room accesses a rear deck and uses windows and French doors for natural illumination.

KITCHEN — Wraparound countertops become instant gathering spots for snacking and chatting, while also creating an attractive partition between rooms.

PATIO

storage

walk-in closet

BED RM.
13-4 x 16-0

cl

BED RM.
12-4 x 12-4

fireplace

REC. RM.
20-0 x 16-0

bath

lin.

up

storage

storage

BASEMENT

BRKFST.
13-0 x 12-8
(vaulted ceiling)

DECK

DECK

lin.

seat

master bath

MASTER BED RM.
14-0 x 16-0

KITCHEN
13-4 x 16-0

fireplace

GREAT RM.
21-0 x 16-0
(cathedral ceiling)

SCREEN PORCH
11-10 x 15-8
(cathedral ceiling)

walk-in closet

pan.

lin.

sto.

walk-in closet

w d

UTIL.
9-8 x 8-0

storage

DINING
13-0 x 12-4

down

FOYER
14-10 x 5-8

bath

lin.

cl

cl

PORCH

BED RM./ STUDY
11-0 x 13-0

FIRST FLOOR

GARAGE
21-8 x 25-8

REAR VIEW — Porches, columns and a single dormer unite for a captivating façade that easily mirrors the allure of the front exterior.

TO ORDER CALL:
1-866-525-9374

PLAN#:
DHDG01-866-D

Adelaide

TOTAL LIVING	FIRST FLOOR	BASEMENT	BED	BATH	WIDTH	DEPTH	FOUNDATION	PRICE CODE
3301 sq. ft.	2151 sq. ft.	1150 sq. ft.	4	3	83'0"	74'4"	Hillside Walkout	G

Home photographed may differ from construction documents.

VACATION/WATERFRONT

Briarcliff Cottage

© 2003 FRANK BETZ ASSOCIATES, INC.

PLAN# DHFB01-3784   1-866-525-9374

With the common rooms open to each other, this floor plan incorporates a natural traffic flow. The kitchen includes a step-saving design, and for added convenience, the utility room lies adjacent to the kitchen. Decorative ceiling treatments, such as the coffered ceiling in the family room and the vaulted ceiling in the keeping room, help to differentiate these spaces. The lower level with a secondary kitchen, fireplace and built-in cabinetry for media equipment is an entertaining family's dream. The garage entrance is conveniently located near the stairway, making the lower level incredibly accessible.

FOYER — High ceilings and crown molding welcome guests into the *Briarcliff Cottage*.

MASTER BEDROOM — A coffered ceiling enhances the master bedroom by adding architectural interest and visually expanding the space.

DINING ROOM — The absence of doors and the triple window with transoms lighten the dining room, allowing natural light to spill into the foyer.

BASEMENT KITCHEN — Striking red cabinetry and modern light fixtures create a contemporary ambiance in this secondary kitchen.

REAR ELEVATION

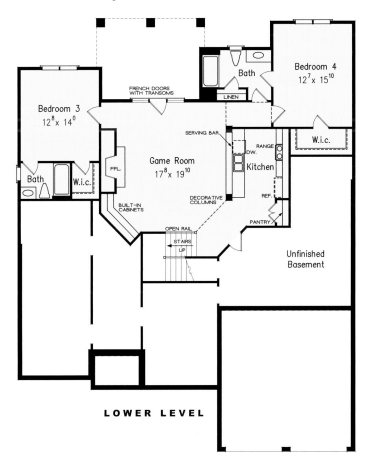

LOWER LEVEL

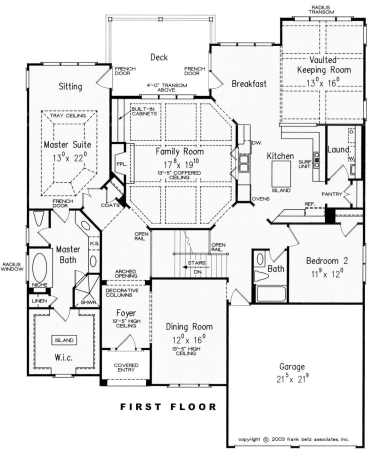

FIRST FLOOR

copyright © 2003 frank betz associates, inc.

TO ORDER CALL: 1-866-525-9374	PLAN#: DHFB01-3784	*Briarcliff Cottage*

TOTAL LIVING	FIRST FLOOR	LOWER LEVEL	BED	BATH	WIDTH	DEPTH	FOUNDATION	PRICE CODE
3649 sq. ft.	2391 sq. ft.	1258 sq. ft.	4	4	54'0"	66'0"	Basement	I

Home photographed may differ from construction documents.

© 2002 DONALD A. GARDNER, INC.

PLAN# DHDG01-994   **1-866-525-9374**

With Old-World charm, this cottage features stone and cedar shake with shed and eyebrow dormers, and the porch is accented by a single column and twin arches.

Inside, the gathering rooms are open to each other, individually distinguished by columns and ceiling treatments. Both the foyer and great room have two-story ceilings that are brightened by dormers, and the fireplace is flanked by built-in cabinetry. The breakfast nook includes two pantries, while the kitchen features a cooktop island.

Upstairs, a balcony separates two additional bedrooms, and a flexible bonus room can accommodate a family's growing needs or wishes.

DINING ROOM — The tray ceiling in the dining room provides additional luxury to this formal room.

GREAT ROOM — Columns frame the entry into the great room that features an impressive array of windows and custom details.

KITCHEN — Dark cabinetry with light-colored countertops combine for a sophisticated look in the kitchen, while stainless steel appliances grant a modern feel.

REAR VIEW — Showcasing an optional walk-out basement, the rear view is complete with several decks and windows that give it an impressive exterior.

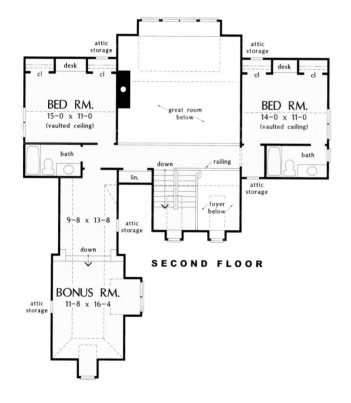

SECOND FLOOR

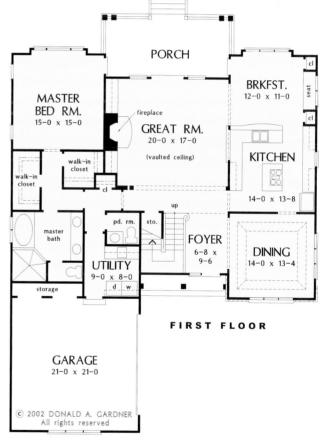

FIRST FLOOR

*Other foundation options available. See page 255

TO ORDER CALL: 1-866-525-9374	PLAN#: DHDG01-994	*Newcastle*

TOTAL LIVING	FIRST FLOOR	SECOND FLOOR	BONUS	BED	BATH	WIDTH	DEPTH	FOUNDATION	PRICE CODE
2515 sq. ft.	1834 sq. ft.	681 sq. ft.	365 sq. ft.	3	3-1/2	50'8"	66'8"	Crawl Space*	F

Home photographed may differ from construction documents.

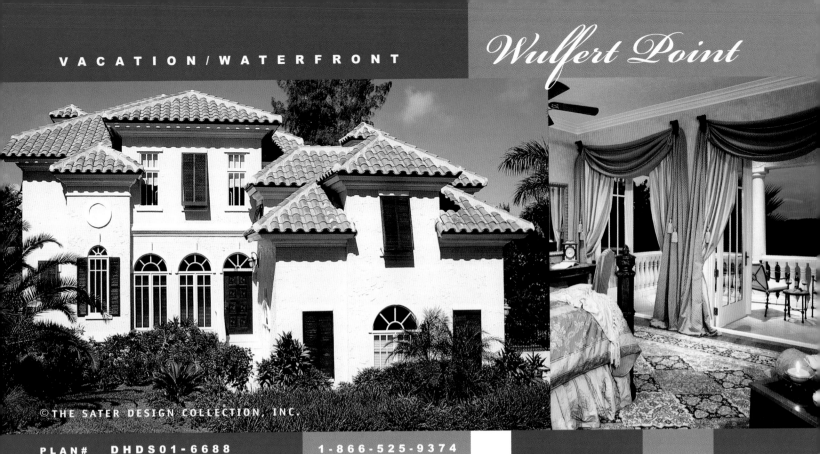

©THE SATER DESIGN COLLECTION, INC.

PLAN# DHDS01-6688   1-866-525-9374

A Charleston Row courtyard complete with a sundeck, spa and lap pool make this charming villa a relaxing retreat. The Spanish tile roof and stucco exterior evoke memories of vacations past, and louvered shutters and circle head windows further enhance the exterior. French doors extend the living areas and welcome balmy breezes inside.

Arches and columns announce interior vistas as well as multi-directional views. In the great room, French doors extend an invitation to the porch, sundeck and courtyard. A bayed formal dining room opens to the kitchen, which shares its own views.

The second level includes two secondary bedrooms and a grand master suite with walls of glass that bring the outside in. A bonus room over the garage could be built as a home theater or office.

GREAT ROOM — A barrel-vaulted gallery hall leads to a spacious great room through the formal dining room and gourmet kitchen. Rows of windows and a series of French doors allow abundant sunlight and fresh air.

KITCHEN — Wrapping counters and a food-preparation island permit easy conversations with guests, and a view of the courtyard through the dining room's bay window.

COURTYARD — Stepping-stone tiles create a walkway over the lap pool. The Palladian-style window above the fountain permits views of the courtyard from the bonus room.

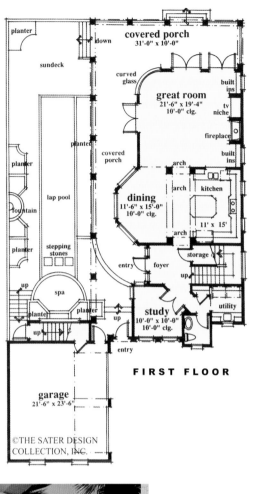

FIRST FLOOR

©THE SATER DESIGN COLLECTION, INC.

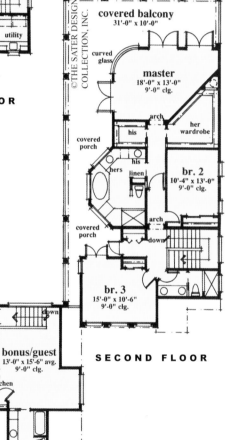

SECOND FLOOR

PORCH — Square columns anchor the views from a sitting area of the wraparound porch. Around the corner, a lush court-yard unfolds around a lap pool, planters and a garden fountain.

TO ORDER CALL: 1-866-525-9374	PLAN#: DHDS01-6688	*Wulfert Point*

TOTAL LIVING	FIRST FLOOR	SECOND FLOOR	BONUS ROOM	BED	BATH	WIDTH	DEPTH	FOUNDATION	PRICE CODE
2873 sq. ft.	1293 sq. ft.	1154 sq. ft.	426 sq. ft.	4	3-1/2	50'0"	90'0"	Slab	G

Home photographed may differ from construction documents.

©*The Sater Design Collection, Inc.*

© THE SATER DESIGN COLLECTION, INC.

PLAN# DHDS01-6808   **1-866-525-9374**

This charming cottage evokes a bygone era with fresh white shutters and periwinkle blue siding, yet features the best modern conveniences in an impressive floor plan. The home's vibrant interior emphasizes a central fireplace, high ceilings that rise to an open balcony and a wall of windows that illuminate the living areas with views.

Taking center stage, the comfortable and open great room expands into the adjoining kitchen and dining areas — defined by decorative columns. A vaulted ceiling visually enlarges this space. Two ample guest bedrooms also share the main floor while the upstairs is dedicated solely to the private master suite. Typical of Southern architecture, this coastal cottage is designed for a tropical climate with its many doors and windows. Nearly every room has either outdoor views or porch access.

GREAT ROOM — Wide open spaces are strengthened with pillars and panes of glass.

DINING ROOM — Artfully decorated, the spaces blend together seamlessly. A square archway frames the sitting area beyond the dining room.

KITCHEN — The inviting kitchen — complete with a double oven, pantry and rows of Shaker style cabinets — will make even a novice cook feel like a chef.

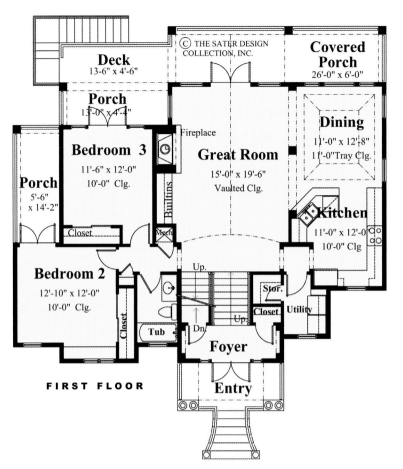

FIRST FLOOR

- Deck 13'-6" x 4'-6"
- Porch 13'-0" x 4'-4"
- © THE SATER DESIGN COLLECTION, INC.
- Covered Porch 26'-0" x 6'-0"
- Dining 11'-0" x 12'-8" 11'-0" Tray Clg.
- Fireplace
- Bedroom 3 11'-6" x 12'-0" 10'-0" Clg.
- Great Room 15'-0" x 19'-6" Vaulted Clg.
- Builtins
- Porch 5'-6" x 14'-2"
- Closet
- Mech.
- Kitchen 11'-0" x 12'-0" 10'-0" Clg
- Bedroom 2 12'-10" x 12'-0" 10'-0" Clg.
- Up.
- Stor.
- Closet
- Utility
- Closet
- Tub
- Dn.
- Up.
- Foyer
- Entry

SECOND FLOOR

- Porch 13'-6" x 4'-10"
- Open to Below 18'-0" Vaulted Clg.
- Master Suite 12'-8" x 17'-8" 10'-0" tray clg.
- © THE SATER DESIGN COLLECTION, INC.
- W.I.C.
- Overlook
- Linen
- Walk-in Shower
- Master Bath
- Dn.
- Dn.
- Whirlpool
- Porch 12'-8" x 4'-8"

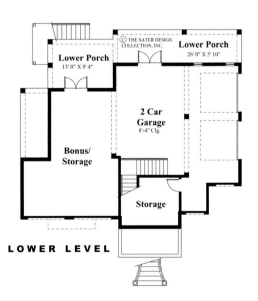

LOWER LEVEL

- Lower Porch 13'-0" X 9'-4"
- © THE SATER DESIGN COLLECTION, INC.
- Lower Porch 26'-0" X 5'-10"
- Bonus/ Storage
- 2 Car Garage 8'-4" Clg.
- Storage

REAR VIEW — Typical of southern architecture this coastal cottage is designed for a tropical climate with its many doors and windows.

TO ORDER CALL: 1-866-525-9374	PLAN#: DHDS01-6808	*Santa Rosa*

TOTAL LIVING	FIRST FLOOR	SECOND FLOOR	BED	BATH	WIDTH	DEPTH	FOUNDATION	PRICE CODE
1978 sq. ft.	1383 sq. ft.	595 sq. ft.	3	2	48'0"	42'0"	Island Basement	F

Home photographed may differ from construction documents.

© 1999 FRANK BETZ ASSOCIATES, INC.

PLAN# DHFB01-1236   **1-866-525-9374**

From the *Southern Living® Design Collection* — This quaint one-story design combines classic architectural detail with a charming cottage feel. Elegant columns grace the front porch to create an inviting entry, while bright windows and a wide center gable offer a memorable first impression. Inside, a formal living and dining room make ideal gathering spaces for a delightful holiday meal or a private library. The expansive master suite features a tray ceiling and bright windows. The master bath is complete with his-and-her vanities, a vaulted ceiling and spacious walk-in closet.

FAMILY ROOM — The family room is marked by an arched opening flanked by columns for a sense of arrival.

KITCHEN — Plenty of counter space and a serving bar are easily accessible from the family room.

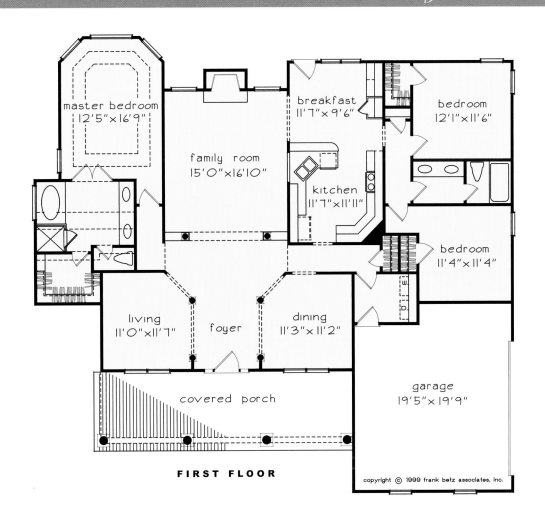

FIRST FLOOR

- master bedroom 12'5"×16'9"
- family room 15'0"×16'10"
- breakfast 11'7"×9'6"
- bedroom 12'1"×11'6"
- kitchen 11'7"×11'11"
- bedroom 11'4"×11'4"
- living 11'0"×11'7"
- foyer
- dining 11'3"×11'2"
- covered porch
- garage 19'5"×19'9"

copyright © 1999 frank betz associates, inc.

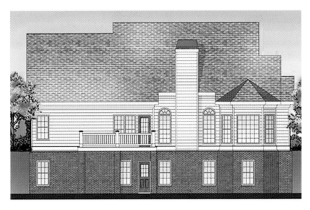

REAR ELEVATION

TO ORDER CALL: 1-866-525-9374	PLAN#: DHFB01-1236	*New Albany*

TOTAL LIVING	FIRST FLOOR	SECOND FLOOR	BED	BATH	WIDTH	DEPTH	FOUNDATION	PRICE CODE
1920 sq. ft.	1920 sq. ft.	N/A	3	2	59'0"	54'6"	Basement, Crawl Space or Slab	G

Home photographed may differ from construction documents.

©1999 Frank Betz Associates, Inc.

Cedar Crest

© CORNERSTONE DESIGNS, LLC

PLAN# DHCS01-M4100A3S-0   1-866-525-9374

A Craftsman masterpiece, the *Cedar Crest* is perfect for a forest or fairway lot. Its wraparound porch adds warmth to the façade and is a great place to watch the world go by. A side-entry garage and decorative shop bay further enhance its curb appeal.

The popular family living layout features vaulted formal living and dining rooms off the volume foyer, complemented by a spacious informal living area with a covered patio that is ideal for outdoor dining.

The angled front stair leads directly to the luxury master suite with its private sitting room and grand bath. A second stair provides quiet access to the children's bedrooms with connecting bath, guest suite with private bath, and large vaulted bonus room.

The *Cedar Crest's* romantic façade and easy-living floor plan create a dramatic expression of "home".

FORMAL FOYER — Dramatic ceiling vaults, wainscots and columns grace the *Cedar Crest's* formal rooms. Wide, high windows bring light deep into the space and connect with the wraparound front porch. The built-in hutch is an elegant touch.

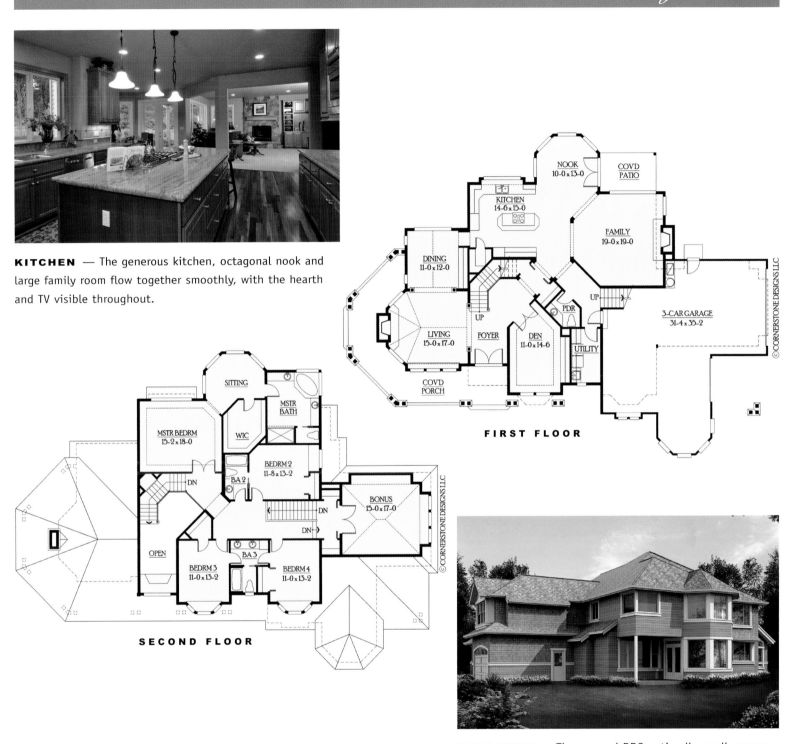

KITCHEN — The generous kitchen, octagonal nook and large family room flow together smoothly, with the hearth and TV visible throughout.

FIRST FLOOR

NOOK
10-0 x 13-0

COVD
PATIO

KITCHEN
14-6 x 15-0

FAMILY
19-0 x 19-0

DINING
11-0 x 12-0

UP

3-CAR GARAGE
31-4 x 35-2

PDR

UP

LIVING
15-0 x 17-0

FOYER

DEN
11-0 x 14-6

UTILITY

COVD
PORCH

©CORNERSTONE DESIGNS LLC

SECOND FLOOR

SITTING

MSTR
BATH

MSTR BEDRM
15-2 x 18-0

WIC

DN

BA 2

BEDRM 2
11-8 x 13-2

BONUS
15-0 x 17-0

DN

DN

OPEN

BEDRM 3
11-0 x 13-2

BA 3

BEDRM 4
11-0 x 13-2

©CORNERSTONE DESIGNS LLC

REAR VIEW — The covered BBQ patio allows all-season outdoor living, while expansive windows on both floors capture light and views of nature.

TO ORDER CALL: 1-866-525-9374	PLAN#:DHCS01-M4100A3S-0		*Cedar Crest*

TOTAL LIVING	FIRST FLOOR	SECOND FLOOR	BED	BATH	WIDTH	DEPTH	FOUNDATION	PRICE CODE
4100 sq. ft.	2010 sq. ft.	2090 sq. ft.	4	3-1/2	90'0"	66'6"	Crawl Space	H

Home photographed may differ from construction documents.

©CornerStone Designs, LLC

Crowne Canyon

© 1998 DONALD A. GARDNER, INC.

PLAN# DHDG01-732-D   1-866-525-9374

A stunning center dormer with arched window and decorative wood brackets cap the entry to this extraordinary hillside estate.

Exposed wood beams enhance the magnificent cathedral ceilings of the foyer, great room, dining room, master bedroom and screened porch, while ten-foot ceilings top the remainder of the first floor. The great room takes in scenic rear views through a wall of windows shared by the media/rec room. Fireplaces add warmth and ambience to the great room, media/rec room, screened porch and the master suite's study/sitting.

The kitchen is complete with its center island cook-top, pantry and ample room for two or more cooks. A three-and-a-half car garage allows space for storage or a golf cart.

GREAT ROOM — Exposed beams draw the eye upward, as does the colossal stone fireplace in the great room. An adjacent sitting area overlooks the balcony and provides additional space to relax.

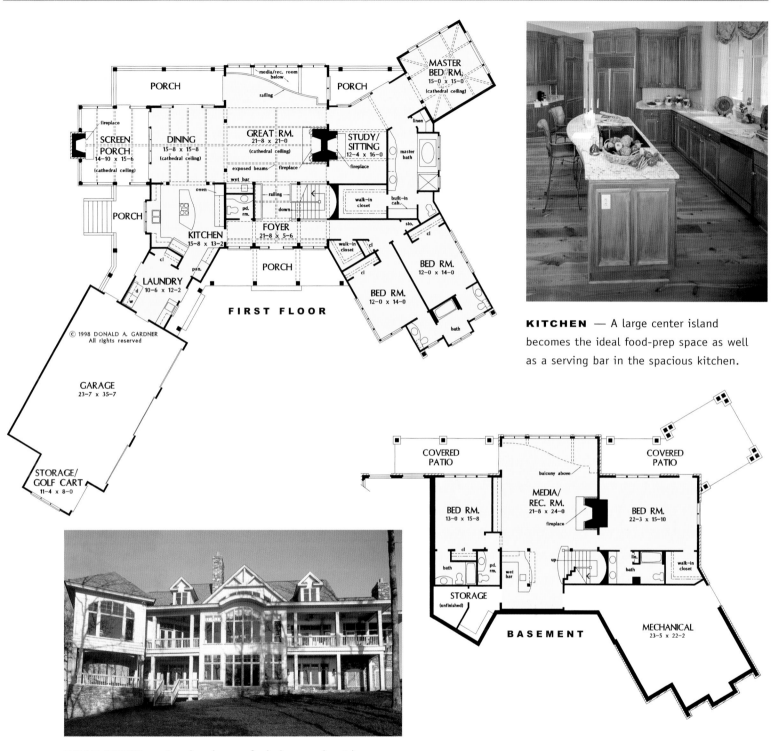

FIRST FLOOR

PORCH

media/rec. room below

railing

PORCH

MASTER BED RM.
15-0 x 15-0
(cathedral ceiling)

fireplace

SCREEN PORCH
14-10 x 15-6
(cathedral ceiling)

DINING
15-8 x 15-8
(cathedral ceiling)

GREAT RM.
21-8 x 21-0
(cathedral ceiling)

STUDY/ SITTING
12-4 x 16-0

linen

master bath

exposed beams   fireplace

fireplace

PORCH

wet bar

oven

railing   down

walk-in closet

built-in cab.

KITCHEN
15-8 x 13-2

pd. rm.

FOYER
21-8 x 5-6

slo.

cl

PORCH

walk-in closet

cl

BED RM.
12-0 x 14-0

LAUNDRY
10-6 x 12-2

pan.

cl

BED RM.
12-0 x 14-0

bath

GARAGE
23-7 x 35-7

STORAGE/ GOLF CART
11-4 x 8-0

COVERED PATIO

balcony above

COVERED PATIO

BED RM.
13-0 x 15-8

MEDIA/ REC. RM.
21-8 x 24-0

fireplace

BED RM.
22-3 x 15-10

cl

up

lin.

bath

pd. rm.

wet bar

bath

walk-in closet

STORAGE
(unfinished)

BASEMENT

MECHANICAL
23-5 x 22-2

KITCHEN — A large center island becomes the ideal food-prep space as well as a serving bar in the spacious kitchen.

REAR VIEW — An abundance of windows and outdoor living spaces give the rear exterior an impressive façade.

TO ORDER CALL: 1-866-525-9374	PLAN#: DHDG01-732-D	*Crowne Canyon*

TOTAL LIVING	FIRST FLOOR	BASEMENT	BED	BATH	WIDTH	DEPTH	FOUNDATION	PRICE CODE
4776 sq. ft.	3040 sq. ft.	1736 sq. ft.	5	4F/2H	106'5"	104'2"	Hillside Walkout	J

Home photographed may differ from construction documents.

Nassau Cove

PLAN#: DHDS01-6654						**TO ORDER CALL:** 1-866-525-9374		

©*The Sater Design Collection, Inc.*

TOTAL LIVING	FIRST FLOOR	SECOND FLOOR	BED	BATH	WIDTH	DEPTH	FOUNDATION	PRICE CODE
1853 sq. ft.	1342 sq. ft.	511 sq. ft.	3	2	44'0"	40'0"	Island Basement	E

This elevated home is a cozy cottage ideal for a family or vacation retreat. Inside, the entry opens into the grand room, it is the perfect gathering spot. The welcoming room has a fireplace, a vaulted ceiling and French doors to the deck. The kitchen and dining room are kept open to keep with the spacious feel of the home.

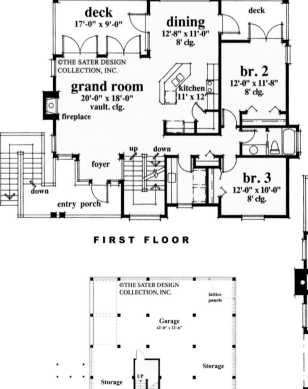

FIRST FLOOR

LOWER LEVEL

SECOND FLOOR

TO ORDER CALL: 1-866-525-9374	PLAN#: DHDS01-6701	*Duvall Street*

TOTAL LIVING	FIRST FLOOR	SECOND FLOOR	BED	BATH	WIDTH	DEPTH	FOUNDATION	PRICE CODE
2123 sq. ft.	878 sq. ft.	1245 sq. ft.	3	2-1/2	27'6"	64'0"	Crawl Space	F

©The Sater Design Collection, Inc.

Home photographed may differ from construction documents.

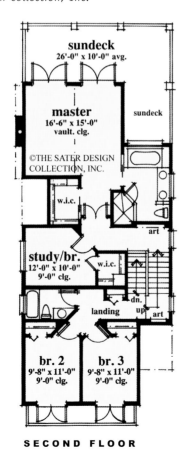

SECOND FLOOR

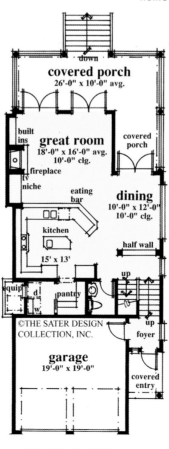

FIRST FLOOR

Wide steps lead up to the charming front porch. Inside, French doors open the great room to views and extend the living areas to the back porch. The gourmet kitchen boasts a prep sink, plenty of counter space and an eating bar. The mid-level landing leads to two secondary bedrooms, a full bath and a windowed art niche.

REAR VIEW

Tucker Town Way

PLAN#: DHDS01-6692

TO ORDER CALL: 1-866-525-9374

TOTAL LIVING	FIRST FLOOR	LOWER LEVEL	BED	BATH	WIDTH	DEPTH	FOUNDATION	PRICE CODE
2190 sq. ft.	2190 sq. ft.	N/A	3	2	59'8"	54'0"	Island Basement	F

©The Sater Design Collection, Inc.

The arched entry of this Southampton-style cottage borrows freely from its Southern coastal past. The foyer opens up to the spacious grand room, which features a fireplace, built-ins and French doors to the lanai. A well-crafted kitchen boasts wrapping counter space, a casual eating bar, a corner walk-in pantry and easy access to the formal dining room.

REAR ELEVATION

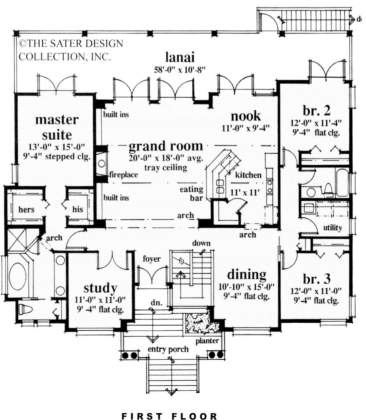

FIRST FLOOR

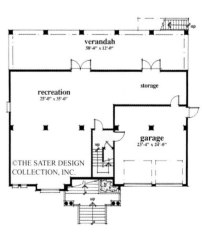

LOWER LEVEL

TO ORDER CALL: 1-866-525-9374	PLAN#: DHDS01-6684						*Southhampton Bay*	

TOTAL LIVING	FIRST FLOOR	LOWER LEVEL	BED	BATH	WIDTH	DEPTH	FOUNDATION	PRICE CODE
2465 sq. ft.	2385 sq. ft.	80 sq. ft.	3	2-1/2	60'4"	59'4"	Slab	F

©*The Sater Design Collection, Inc.*

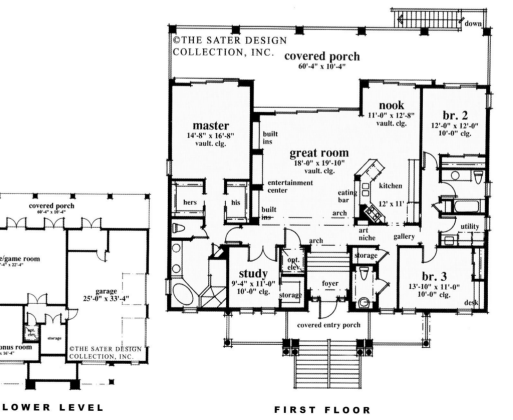

LOWER LEVEL

FIRST FLOOR

A cupola on this gorgeous coastal design tops a pediment and low-pitched roof. Inside, natural light and views pour into the entire rear of the home through glass doors and windows. The spacious great room features built-ins, a vaulted ceiling and an eating bar connecting to the kitchen. A split-floor plan provides privacy for the master and secondary bedrooms.

REAR ELEVATION

Mission Hills

	PLAN#:		TO ORDER CALL:
	DHDS01-6845		1-866-525-9374

TOTAL LIVING	FIRST FLOOR	LOWER LEVEL	BED	BATH	WIDTH	DEPTH	FOUNDATION	PRICE CODE
2494 sq. ft.	2385 sq. ft.	109 sq. ft.	3	3	60'0"	52'0"	Island Basement	F

©The Sater Design Collection, Inc.

This enticing European villa boasts an Italian charm and a distinctly Mediterranean feel. Inside, the foyer steps led up to the formal living areas. Vaulted ceiling create a sense of spaciousness throughout the home, and enhance the interior vistas provided by the central great room, which overlooks the rear deck. The island kitchen is conveniently open to a breakfast nook.

REAR ELEVATION

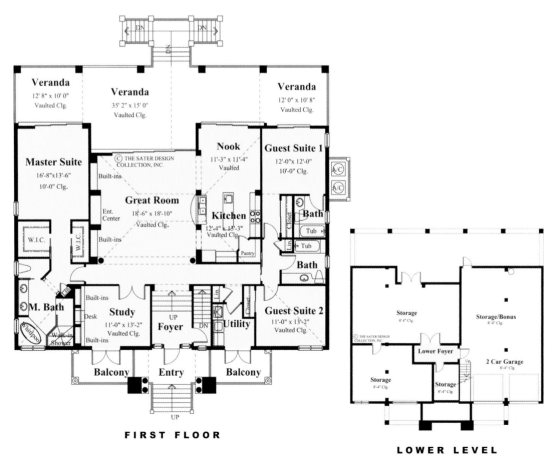

FIRST FLOOR

LOWER LEVEL

TO ORDER CALL:	PLAN#:	*Carmel Bay*
1-866-525-9374	DHDS01-6810	

TOTAL LIVING	FIRST FLOOR	SECOND FLOOR	BED	BATH	WIDTH	DEPTH	FOUNDATION	PRICE CODE
2513 sq. ft.	1542 sq. ft.	971 sq. ft.	4	3	46'0"	51'0"	Island Basement	G

©The Sater Design Collection, Inc.

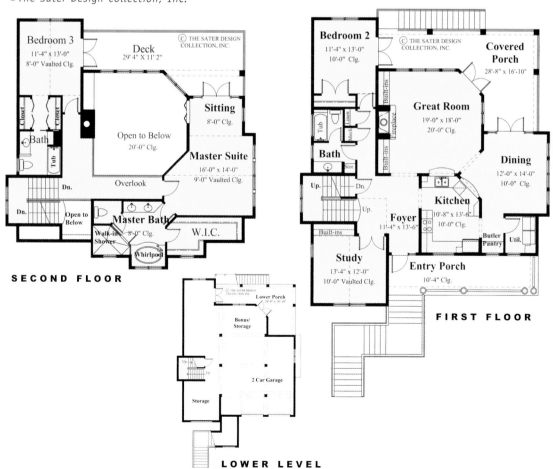

SECOND FLOOR

- Bedroom 3 — 11'-4" x 13'-0" — 8'-0" Vaulted Clg.
- Deck — 29' 4" X 11' 2"
- Sitting — 8'-0" Clg.
- Open to Below — 20'-0" Clg.
- Master Suite — 16'-0" x 14'-0" — 9'-0" Vaulted Clg.
- Overlook
- Master Bath — 8'-0" Clg.
- Walk-in Shower
- Whirlpool
- W.I.C.
- Bath
- Closet

FIRST FLOOR

- Bedroom 2 — 11'-4" x 13'-0" — 10'-0" Clg.
- Covered Porch — 28'-8" x 16'-10"
- Great Room — 19'-0" x 18'-0" — 20'-0" Clg.
- Dining — 12'-0" x 14'-0" — 10'-0" Clg.
- Kitchen — 10'-8" x 13'-6" — 10'-0" Clg.
- Butler Pantry
- Util.
- Foyer — 11'-4" x 13'-6"
- Study — 13'-4" x 12'-0" — 10'-0" Vaulted Clg.
- Entry Porch — 10'-4" Clg.
- Bath
- Built-ins

LOWER LEVEL

- Lower Porch — 20'-4" x 16'-10"
- Bonus/Storage
- 2 Car Garage
- Storage

The foyer announces an open arrangement of casual space and formal rooms. French doors lead to a quiet study or parlor, which features a wall of built-in shelves and an arched window that views the front property. Built-ins frame the fireplace in the great room, providing an anchor for the wall of glass that creates a connection with the outdoors.

REAR ELEVATION

Bridgeport Harbor

	PLAN#:					TO ORDER CALL:	
	DHDS01-6685					1-866-525-9374	

TOTAL LIVING	FIRST FLOOR	SECOND FLOOR	BED	BATH	WIDTH	DEPTH	FOUNDATION	PRICE CODE
2520 sq. ft.	1305 sq. ft.	1215 sq. ft.	3	2-1/2	30'6"	77'6"	Slab	G

©The Sater Design Collection, Inc.

Jamaican plantation houses inspired this cottage design, lovingly revived by the Old Charleston Row homes. Wraparound porticos on two levels offer views to the living areas, while a deck for stargazing opens from the master suite. French doors bring the outside in to the great room, which features a fireplace, built-ins and an eating bar connecting to the kitchen.

REAR ELEVATION

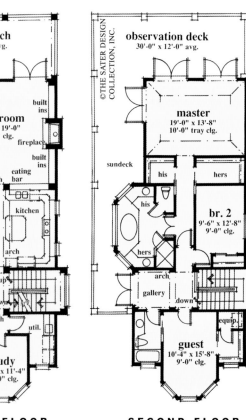

FIRST FLOOR

SECOND FLOOR

LOWER LEVEL

TO ORDER CALL: 1-866-525-9374		PLAN#: DHDS01-6827			*Sommerset*				
TOTAL LIVING	**FIRST FLOOR**	**SECOND FLOOR**	**BED**	**BATH**	**WIDTH**	**DEPTH**	**FOUNDATION**		**PRICE CODE**
2650 sq. ft.	1296 sq. ft.	1354 sq. ft.	3	2-1/2	34'0"	63'2"	Slab		**G**

©The Sater Design Collection, Inc.

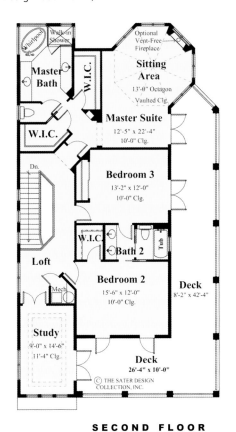

SECOND FLOOR

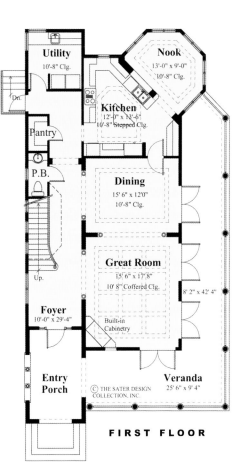

FIRST FLOOR

An elegant portico and deck enhance the outdoor flow of this enchanting manor. All of the living spaces have French doors that open to the porch. A gallery-style foyer leads to a powder room and a walk-in pantry, which enhances the efficiency of the kitchen. Wrapping counter space provides an overlook to a breakfast bay and 180-degree views of the rear property.

REAR ELEVATION

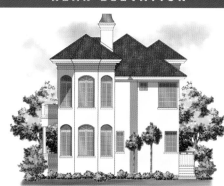

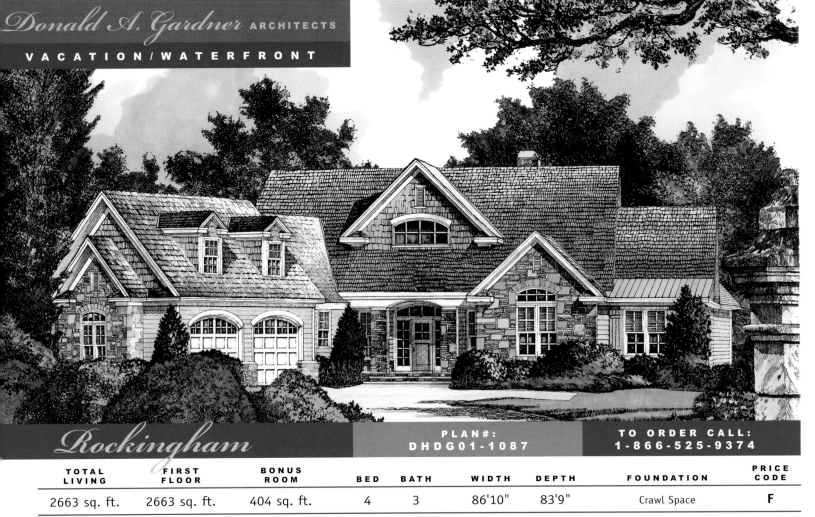

Rockingham

	PLAN#:	TO ORDER CALL:
	DHDG01-1087	1-866-525-9374

TOTAL LIVING	FIRST FLOOR	BONUS ROOM	BED	BATH	WIDTH	DEPTH	FOUNDATION	PRICE CODE
2663 sq. ft.	2663 sq. ft.	404 sq. ft.	4	3	86'10"	83'9"	Crawl Space	F

©2004 Donald A. Gardner, Inc.

Because some families enjoy a seamless progression between entertaining spaces, this home's kitchen, dining room and great room all overflow into one another. Enjoying outdoor meals is easy, as a screen porch and two adjacent porches are positioned just off the dining room.

REAR ELEVATION

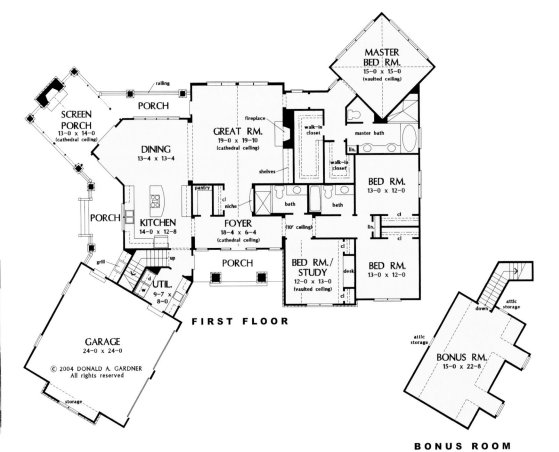

FIRST FLOOR

BONUS ROOM

TO ORDER CALL: 1-866-525-9374	PLAN#: DHFB01-3766	*Breyerton*						
TOTAL LIVING	**FIRST FLOOR**	**SECOND FLOOR**	**BED**	**BATH**	**WIDTH**	**DEPTH**	**FOUNDATION**	**PRICE CODE**
2723 sq. ft.	1847 sq. ft.	876 sq. ft.	4	3-1/2	56'4"	50'6"	Basement, Crawl Space or Slab	**I**

©2002 Frank Betz Associates, Inc.

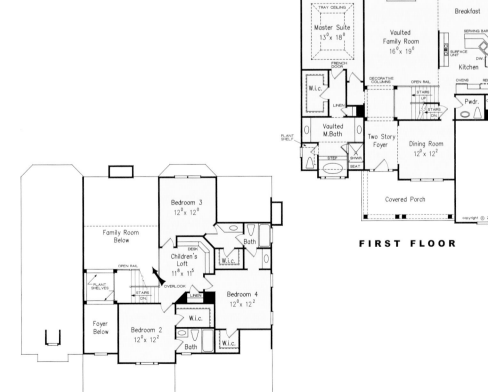

FIRST FLOOR

SECOND FLOOR

The *Breyerton* was designed with today's family in mind, incorporating features that make everyday living more convenient. A keeping room is connected to the kitchen area, providing a great place to spend casual family time. A coat closet and laundry room are just inside the garage, keeping shoes and coats where they belong. Each secondary bedroom adjoins the children's loft; a designated spot for homework and computer fun.

REAR ELEVATION

Montserrat			**PLAN#:** DHDS01-6858			**TO ORDER CALL:** 1-866-525-9374		

TOTAL LIVING	FIRST FLOOR	SECOND FLOOR	BED	BATH	WIDTH	DEPTH	FOUNDATION	PRICE CODE
2756 sq. ft.	1855 sq. ft.	901 sq. ft.	3	3-1/2	66'0"	50'0"	Island Basement	H

©The Sater Design Collection, Inc.

This Southern tidewater cottage is charming with an inviting wrap-around front porch. An octagonal great room with a multifaceted vaulted ceiling illuminates the interior. This room boasts a fireplace, a built-in entertainment center and three sets of French doors, which lead outside to a vaulted lanai. The kitchen features a pass-thru to both the lanai and great room.

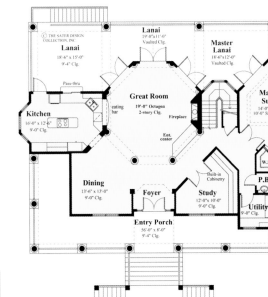

FIRST FLOOR

LOWER LEVEL

REAR ELEVATION

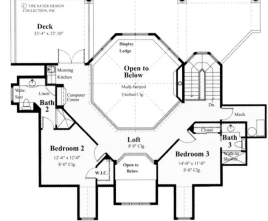

SECOND FLOOR

TO ORDER CALL: 1-866-525-9374	PLAN#: DHFB01-3952	*Summerlake*

TOTAL LIVING	FIRST FLOOR	SECOND FLOOR	BONUS ROOM	BED	BATH	WIDTH	DEPTH	FOUNDATION	PRICE CODE
2899 sq. ft.	2145 sq. ft.	754 sq. ft.	385 sq. ft.	4	3	62'4"	64'0"	Basement, Crawl Space or Slab	I

©2005 Frank Betz Associates, Inc.

FIRST FLOOR

SECOND FLOOR

The spaciousness of the *Summerlake* offers many amenities usually reserved for much larger homes. The luxurious main-level master suite offers a built-in niche, drying area and connecting his-and-her closets with a dressing mirror. An additional bedroom on the main level can be used as such or converted to a study. Upstairs, there are two additional bedrooms, an optional bonus room and a loft with a built-in desk.

REAR ELEVATION

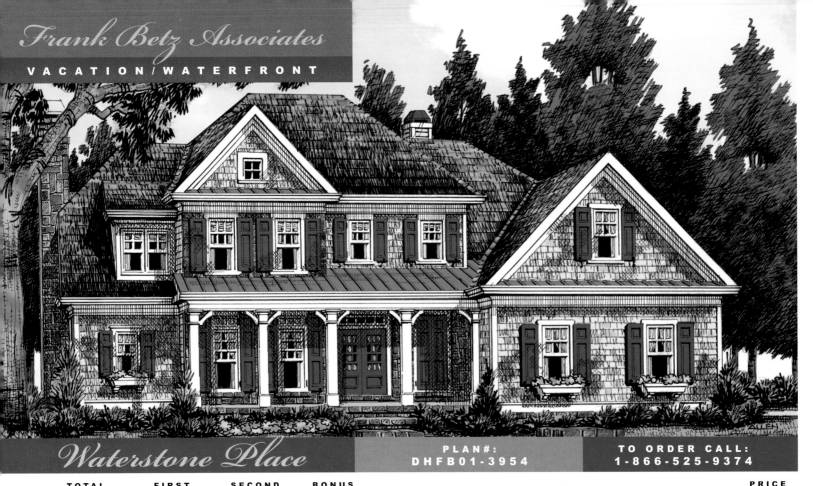

Waterstone Place

	PLAN#:	TO ORDER CALL:
	DHFB01-3954	1-866-525-9374

TOTAL LIVING	FIRST FLOOR	SECOND FLOOR	BONUS ROOM	BED	BATH	WIDTH	DEPTH	FOUNDATION	PRICE CODE
3246 sq. ft.	2260 sq. ft.	986 sq. ft.	510 sq. ft.	4	4-1/2	64'4"	61'0"	Basement or Crawl Space	I

©2005 Frank Betz Associates, Inc.

The cedar shake and front porch are the backdrop for the *Waterstone Place*. The master suite is located on the main level with direct access to the deck. The master bath offers his-and-her walk-in closets, a separate tub and shower. The spacious kitchen has a keeping room with fireplace and a large center island with serving bar and sink.

FIRST FLOOR

REAR ELEVATION

SECOND FLOOR

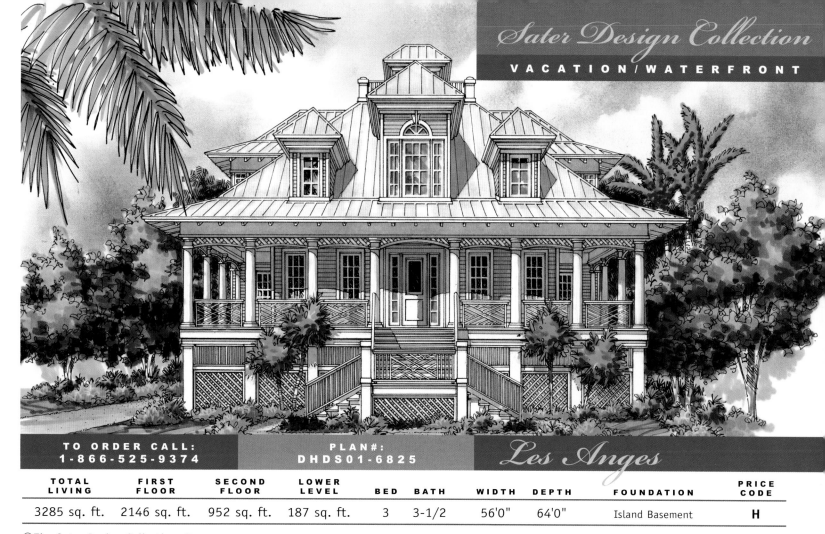

TO ORDER CALL:	PLAN#:	*Les Anges*
1-866-525-9374	DHDS01-6825	

TOTAL LIVING	FIRST FLOOR	SECOND FLOOR	LOWER LEVEL	BED	BATH	WIDTH	DEPTH	FOUNDATION	PRICE CODE
3285 sq. ft.	2146 sq. ft.	952 sq. ft.	187 sq. ft.	3	3-1/2	56'0"	64'0"	Island Basement	H

©*The Sater Design Collection, Inc.*

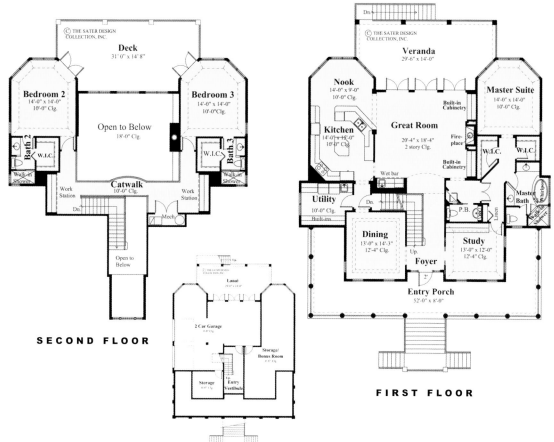

SECOND FLOOR

LOWER LEVEL

FIRST FLOOR

An inviting wraparound porch and additional outdoor spaces extend the living area of this charming cottage. Built-in cabinetry, a massive fireplace and a host of French doors highlight the central living space, which also features a wet bar. The well-designed kitchen includes a sunny breakfast nook, center island, plenty of storage and easy access to the formal dining room.

REAR ELEVATION

Montego Bay

TOTAL LIVING	FIRST FLOOR	SECOND FLOOR	LOWER FOYER	BED	BATH	WIDTH	DEPTH	FOUNDATION	PRICE CODE
3328 sq. ft.	2118 sq. ft.	929 sq. ft.	281 sq. ft.	3	3-1/2	58'0"	54'0"	Island Basement	H

Home photographed may differ from construction documents.

A corner porch provides a cozy place to visit and the rear veranda offers endless entertaining opportunities. Inside, multiple windows infuse almost every room with light and views. The foyer leads into the great room, featuring a two-story coffered ceiling, French doors to the deck and a fireplace surrounded by built-ins. The kitchen boasts a center island and dining nook.

REAR VIEW

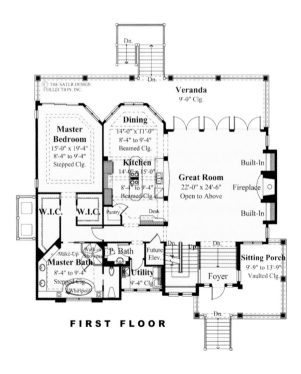

FIRST FLOOR

SECOND FLOOR

LOWER LEVEL

TO ORDER CALL: 1-866-525-9374	PLAN#: DHDG01-995-D	*Laycrest*

TOTAL LIVING	FIRST FLOOR	BASEMENT	BED	BATH	WIDTH	DEPTH	FOUNDATION	PRICE CODE
3397 sq. ft.	1797 sq. ft.	1600 sq. ft.	4	3-1/2	59'0"	59'4"	Hillside Walkout	G

©2002 Donald A. Gardner, Inc.

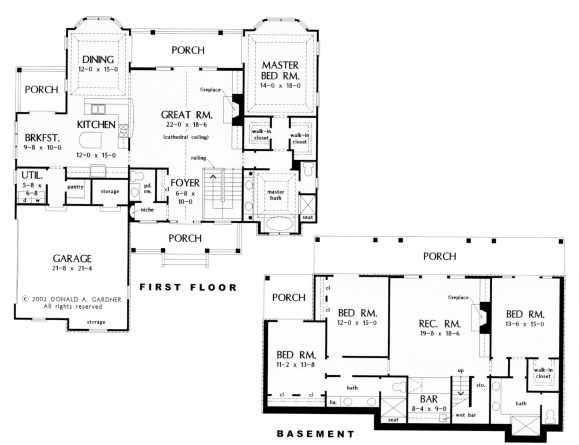

FIRST FLOOR

BASEMENT

With beautiful Arts-and-Crafts charm, this hillside home starts with a striking exterior of siding and stone. A large clerestory window ushers light into the foyer, while every major room is perfectly positioned to take advantage of the views. Built-in cabinetry and fireplaces enhance the great room and rec room, while a wet bar, bay windows and tray ceilings add custom style.

REAR ELEVATION

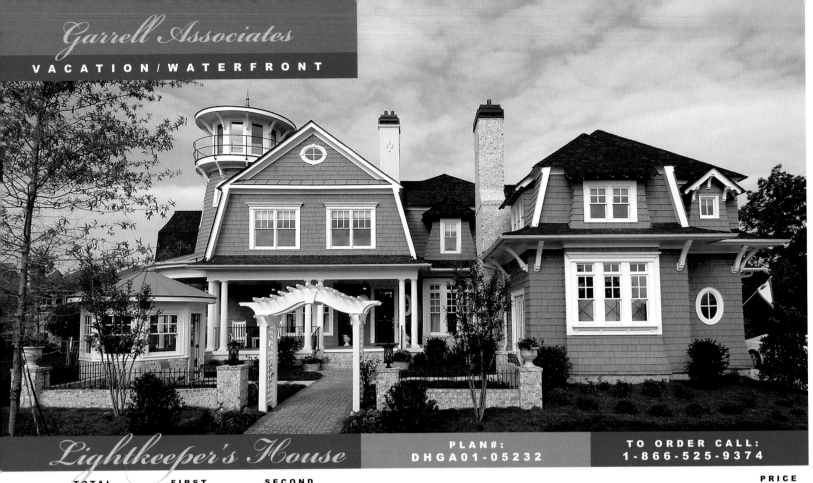

Lightkeeper's House

	PLAN#:	TO ORDER CALL:
	DHGA01-05232	1-866-525-9374

TOTAL LIVING	FIRST FLOOR	SECOND FLOOR	BED	BATH	WIDTH	DEPTH	FOUNDATION	PRICE CODE
6922 sq. ft.	3855 sq. ft.	3067 sq. ft.	6	4-1/2	113'0"	86'6"	Basement/Finished	0

Home photographed may differ from construction documents.

©Garrell Associates, Inc.

The *Lightkeeper's House* alludes to all in a timeless way, yet incorporates all requirements of modern family life in each major space. It is a house with the essence of soul. All it requires is laughter to come alive. This home is filled with unique spaces. The porch extends the area to entertain and can be enjoyed throughout the season.

Smaller version, Beacon Cottage #06309, and Lighthouse Collection also available.

REAR VIEW

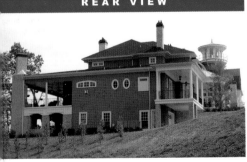

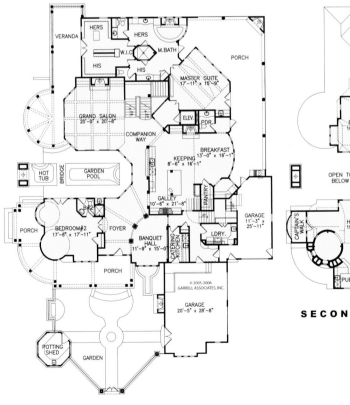

FIRST FLOOR

SECOND FLOOR

| TO ORDER CALL:
1-866-525-9374 | | PLAN#:
DHDG01-1042 | | *Gadberry* | | | | | |

TOTAL LIVING	FIRST FLOOR	BONUS ROOM	BED	BATH	WIDTH	DEPTH	FOUNDATION	PRICE CODE
1986 sq. ft.	1986 sq. ft.	376 sq. ft.	3	2	67'4"	57'8"	Crawl Space	D

Home photographed may differ from construction documents.

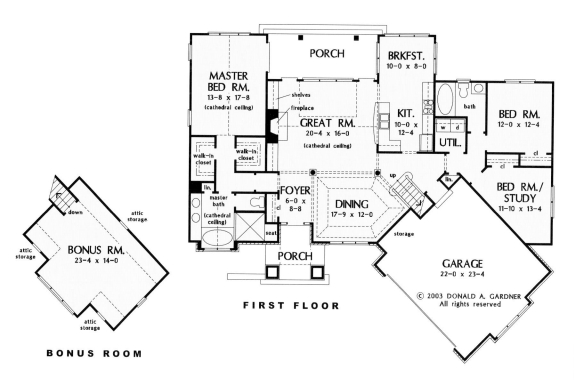

BONUS ROOM

FIRST FLOOR

Cedar shake and stone add Old-World character to this Craftsman cottage. Remarkably open, the floor plan allows every common room to take advantage of rear views. Columns define the dining room, and the tray ceiling expands it. A cathedral ceiling extends from the fireplace to the serving bar. Other special features include built-in cabinetry, a bonus room and French doors.

REAR VIEW

Colemans Bluff

	PLAN#:	TO ORDER CALL:
	DHFB01-3896	1-866-525-9374

TOTAL LIVING	FIRST FLOOR	OPT. SECOND FLOOR	BED	BATH	WIDTH	DEPTH	FOUNDATION	PRICE CODE
2066 sq. ft.	2066 sq. ft.	556 sq. ft.	4	3-1/2	63'0"	79'4"	Basement, Crawl Space or Slab	F

©2004 Frank Betz Associates, Inc.

The *Colemans Bluff* is original and inviting with a coffered ceiling providing a unique canopy over the family room. A large screened porch off the breakfast area provides the perfect spot for outdoor living. The garage entry filters traffic through the mudroom, fully equipped with a coat closet, bench, wall hooks and access to the laundry room.

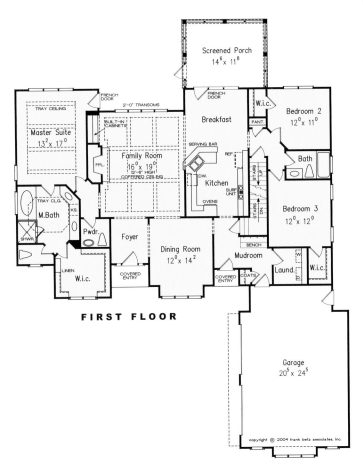

FIRST FLOOR

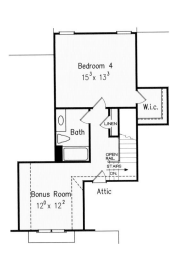

OPT. SECOND FLOOR

REAR ELEVATION

TO ORDER CALL: 1-866-525-9374	PLAN#: DHFB01-3823	Catawba Ridge

TOTAL LIVING	FIRST FLOOR	SECOND FLOOR	BONUS ROOM	BED	BATH	WIDTH	DEPTH	FOUNDATION	PRICE CODE
2389 sq. ft.	1593 sq. ft.	796 sq. ft.	238 sq. ft.	3	3-1/2	59'8"	50'6"	Basement, Crawl Space or Slab	I

©2003 Frank Betz Associates, Inc.

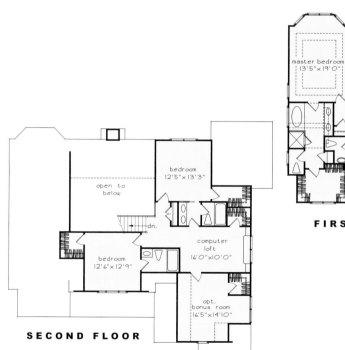

SECOND FLOOR

FIRST FLOOR

From the Southern Living® Design Collection — Charm and character exude from the inviting exterior of *Catawba Ridge* with its thoughtful welcoming of stone and cedar shake. Its kitchen, breakfast area and family room are conveniently grouped together for easy family interaction. Kids will love having their own computer loft. An optional bonus room upstairs is ready to finish as you wish.

REAR ELEVATION

Willow

	PLAN#: DHCS01-M2780B3F-0	TO ORDER CALL: 1-866-525-9374

TOTAL LIVING	FIRST FLOOR	SECOND FLOOR	BED	BATH	WIDTH	DEPTH	FOUNDATION	PRICE CODE
2805 sq. ft.	1330 sq. ft.	1475 sq. ft.	4	2-1/2	40'0"	60'0"	Crawl Space	F

©CornerStone Designs, LLC

A trellised arbor entry invites you to enter this delightful narrow-lot estate. Its compact façade delivers a lot of curb appeal. The *Willow's* stone, shingle, shutter and board-and-batten details create a lively sense of home. The soaring foyer and formal rooms lead to an open family area, covered BBQ porch and private den. The upper floor features a luxury master suite plus three bedrooms and a large bonus room.

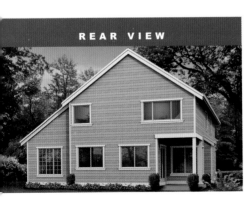

REAR VIEW

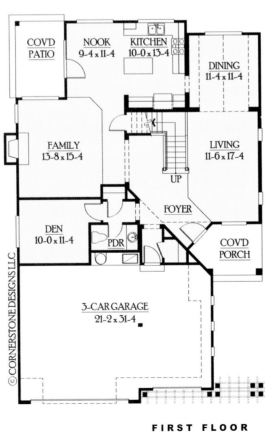

FIRST FLOOR

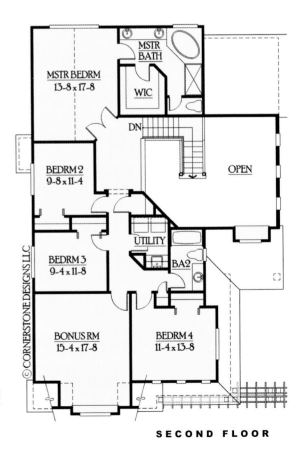

SECOND FLOOR

TO ORDER CALL:
1-866-525-9374

PLAN#:
DHDG01-824-D

Ryecroft

TOTAL LIVING	FIRST FLOOR	BASEMENT	BED	BATH	WIDTH	DEPTH	FOUNDATION	PRICE CODE
2815 sq. ft.	1725 sq. ft.	1090 sq. ft.	3	3-1/2	59'0"	59'4"	Hillside Walkout	F

©1999 Donald A. Gardner, Inc.

Home photographed may differ from construction documents.

FIRST FLOOR

BASEMENT

Arches complement gables on this stylish stone and siding home with a finished walkout basement. Positioning the living areas and master suite on the first floor, a recreational room, wet bar and two bedrooms are on the lower level. An exciting cathedral ceiling expands the foyer and great room, while the dining room and master suite enjoy tray ceilings.

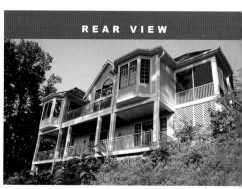

REAR VIEW

Peekskill

											PRICE
TOTAL LIVING	**FIRST FLOOR**	**SECOND FLOOR**	**BASEMENT**	**BONUS ROOM**	**BED**	**BATH**	**WIDTH**	**DEPTH**	**FOUNDATION**		**CODE**
2953 sq. ft.	1662 sq. ft.	585 sq. ft.	706 sq. ft.	575 sq. ft.	4	3-1/2	81'4"	68'8"	Hillside Walkout		**F**

PLAN#:
DHDG01-780-D

TO ORDER CALL:
1-866-525-9374

Home photographed may differ from construction documents.

A center dormer with arched window embellishes the exterior of this hillside walkout. The second-floor balcony overlooks the foyer and great room, while a back porch extends the great room. The master bedroom features porch access, a tray ceiling, built-ins, walk-in closet and private bath. Secondary bedrooms lie upstairs and in the basement. A bonus room resides over the three-car garage.

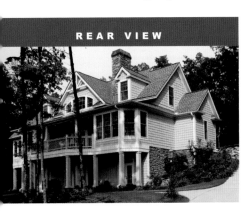

REAR VIEW

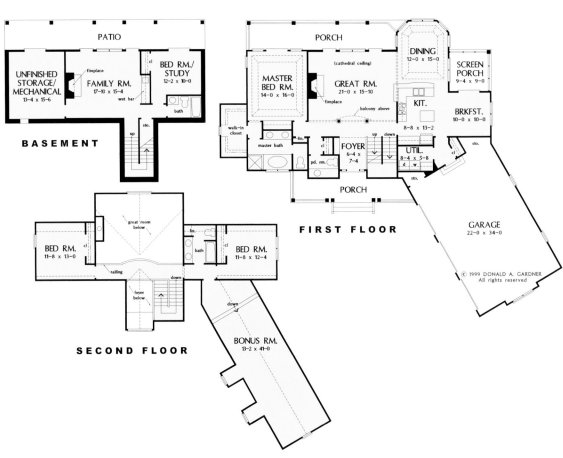

TO ORDER CALL:
1-866-525-9374

PLAN#:
DHDG01-746-D

Vandenberg

TOTAL LIVING	FIRST FLOOR	BASEMENT	BED	BATH	WIDTH	DEPTH	FOUNDATION	PRICE CODE
2956 sq. ft.	1810 sq. ft.	1146 sq. ft.	4	3	68'4"	60'10"	Hillside Walkout	F

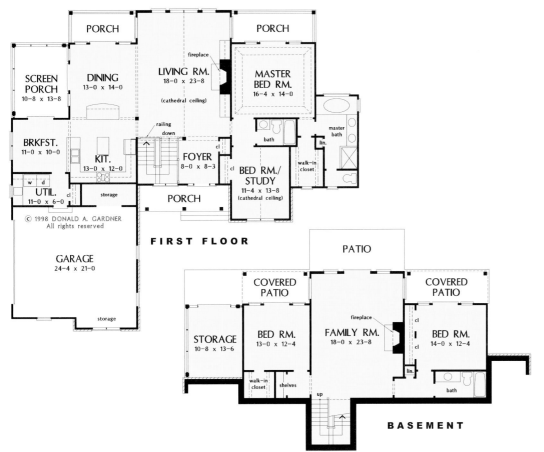

FIRST FLOOR

BASEMENT

This walkout combines stucco, stone and cedar shakes for exceptional character. A dramatic cathedral ceiling heightens the open living room with central fireplace and built-ins. Porches flank the living room to allow its rear wall of windows uninterrupted views. Rear porches are entered through the dining room and master bedroom, while the breakfast and dining rooms enjoy screened-porch access.

REAR ELEVATION

Tillman

	PLAN#:	TO ORDER CALL:
	DHFB01-3953	1-866-525-9374

TOTAL LIVING	FIRST FLOOR	SECOND FLOOR	BONUS ROOM	BED	BATH	WIDTH	DEPTH	FOUNDATION	PRICE CODE
3125 sq. ft.	2399 sq. ft.	726 sq. ft.	425 sq. ft.	4	4	58'4"	72'0"	Basement or Crawl Space	I

©2005 Frank Betz Associates, Inc.

With vertical siding, cedar shakes, stone and brick the *Tillman* embodies all the elements of a truly classic home. The foyer boasts decorative columns to frame the entryway. The open floor plan allows an easy flow from room to room, making entertaining a breeze. A vaulted covered porch and deck allow homeowners to enjoy the outdoors regardless of the weather.

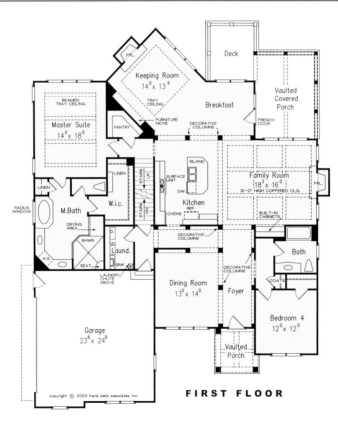

FIRST FLOOR

copyright © 2005 frank betz associates, inc.

SECOND FLOOR

| TO ORDER CALL:
1-866-525-9374 | | PLAN#:
DHDG01-734-D | | | | | | Gilchrist | | |

TOTAL LIVING	FIRST FLOOR	BASEMENT	BONUS ROOM	BED	BATH	WIDTH	DEPTH	FOUNDATION	PRICE CODE
3132 sq. ft.	2094 sq. ft.	1038 sq. ft.	494 sq. ft.	4	3-1/2	62'3"	76'7"	Hillside Walkout	G

©1998 Donald A. Gardner, Inc.

Home photographed may differ from construction documents.

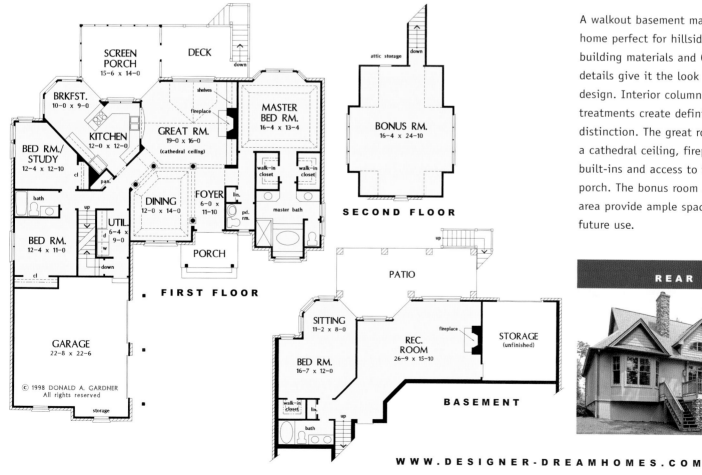

A walkout basement makes this home perfect for hillsides, while its building materials and Craftsman details give it the look of a custom design. Interior columns and ceiling treatments create definition and distinction. The great room features a cathedral ceiling, fireplace, built-ins and access to the screened porch. The bonus room and storage area provide ample space for future use.

REAR VIEW

Frank Betz Associates
VACATION/MOUNTAIN

Lauren Parc

PLAN#: DHFB01-3947					**TO ORDER CALL:** 1-866-525-9374			

TOTAL LIVING	FIRST FLOOR	SECOND FLOOR	BED	BATH	WIDTH	DEPTH	FOUNDATION	PRICE CODE
3591 sq. ft.	2436 sq. ft.	1155 sq. ft.	4	4-1/2	80'0"	65'3"	Basement or Crawl Space	I

©2005 Frank Betz Associates, Inc.

The brick and vertical siding of the *Lauren Parc* is a welcome addition to any neighborhood. Inside is just as amazing. A keeping room with a fireplace is the perfect place to unwind at the end of the day. Tucked behind the kitchen is a walk-in pantry, built-in desk and oversized laundry room complete with a utility sink.

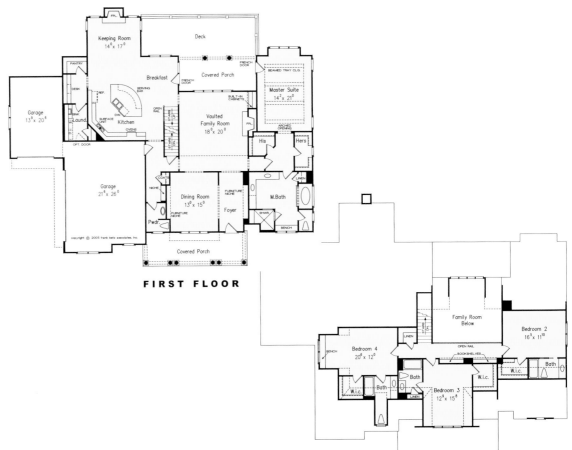

FIRST FLOOR

SECOND FLOOR

REAR ELEVATION

TO ORDER CALL:	PLAN#:	*Bayview*
1-866-525-9374	**DHCS01-M3590B3S-0**	

TOTAL LIVING	FIRST FLOOR	SECOND FLOOR	BED	BATH	WIDTH	DEPTH	FOUNDATION	PRICE CODE
3592 sq. ft.	1761 sq. ft.	1831 sq. ft.	4	3-1/2	77'0"	66'6"	Crawl Space	H

©CornerStone Designs, LLC

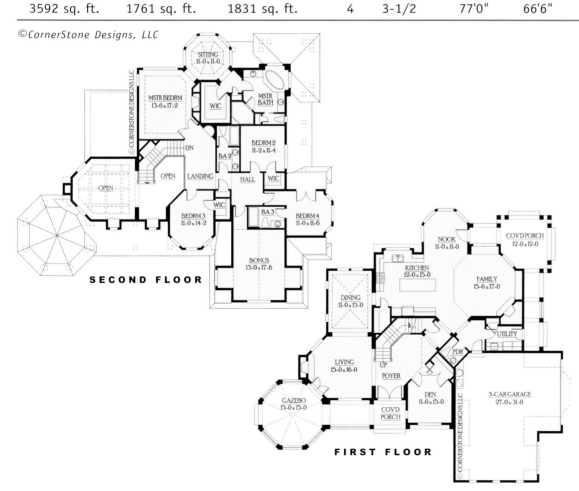

SECOND FLOOR

FIRST FLOOR

This grand Hampton estate creates a feeling of warmth and elegance while providing every modern convenience. The formal rooms and family spaces are connected to the outdoors with generous front and rear covered porches, providing great versatility for entertaining. The grand stair leads to the luxurious master suite with its octagonal sitting room, offering privacy from the bonus room and three secondary bedrooms.

REAR VIEW

Plan Index

PLANS LISTED BY STYLE AND SQUARE FOOTAGE SMALLEST TO LARGEST

Plan Index

BEFORE YOU ORDER

PLEASE READ THE FOLLOWING HELPFUL INFORMATION

QUICK TURNAROUND

Because you are placing your order directly, we can ship plans to you quickly. If your order is placed before noon ET, we can usually have your plans to you the next business day. Some restrictions may apply. We cannot ship to a post office box; please provide a physical street address.

OUR EXCHANGE POLICY

Since our blueprints are printed especially for you at the time you place your order, we cannot accept any returns. If, for some reason, you find that the plan that you purchased does not meet your needs, then you may exchange that plan for another plan in our collection. We allow you sixty days from the time of purchase to make an exchange. At the time of the exchange, you will be charged a processing fee of 20% of the total amount of the original order, plus the difference in price between the plans (if applicable) and the cost to ship the new plans to you. Vellums cannot be exchanged. All sets must be approved and authorization given before the exchange can take place. Please call our customer service department if you have any questions.

LOCAL BUILDING CODES AND ZONING REQUIREMENTS

Our plans are designed to meet or exceed national building standards. Because of the great differences in geography and climate, each state, county and municipality has its own building codes and zoning requirements. Your plan may need to be modified to comply with local requirements regarding snow loads, energy codes, soil and seismic conditions and a wide range of other matters. Prior to using plans ordered from us, we strongly advise that you consult a local building official.

ARCHITECTURE AND ENGINEERING SEALS

Some cities and states are now requiring that a licensed architect or engineer review and approve any set of building documents prior to construction. This is due to concerns over energy costs, safety, structural integrity and other factors. Prior to applying for a building permit or the start of actual construction, we strongly advise that you consult your local building official who can tell you if such a review is required.

DISCLAIMER

We have put substantial care and effort into the creation of our blueprints. We authorize the use of our blueprints on the express condition that you strictly comply with all local building codes, zoning requirements and other applicable laws, regulations and ordinances. However, because we cannot provide on-site consultation, supervision or control over actual construction, and because of the great variance in local building requirements, building practices and soil, seismic, weather and other conditions, WE CANNOT MAKE ANY WARRANTY, EXPRESS OR IMPLIED, WITH RESPECT TO THE CONTENT OR USE OF OUR BLUEPRINTS OR VELLUMS, INCLUDING BUT NOT LIMITED TO ANY WARRANTY OF MERCHANTABILITY OR OF FITNESS FOR A PARTICULAR PURPOSE. Please Note: Floor plans in this book are not construction documents and are subject to change. Renderings are artist's concept only.

HOW MANY SETS OF PRINTS WILL YOU NEED?

We offer a single set of prints so that you can study and plan your dream home in detail. However, you cannot build from this package. One set of blueprints is marked "NOT FOR CONSTRUCTION." If you are planning to obtain estimates from a contractor or subcontractor, or if you are planning to build immediately, you will need more sets. Because additional sets are less expensive, make sure you order enough to satisfy all your requirements. Sometimes changes are needed to a plan; in that case, we offer vellums that are reproducible and erasable so changes can be made directly to the plans. Vellums are the only set that can be reproduced; it is illegal to copy blueprints. The checklist below will help you determine how many sets are needed.

PLAN CHECKLIST

_____ **Owner** (one for notes, one for file)

_____ **Builder** (generally requires at least three sets; one as a legal document, one for inspections and at least one to give subcontractors)

_____ **Local Building Department** (often requires two sets)

_____ **Mortgage Lender** (usually one set for a conventional loan; three sets for FHA or VA loans)

_____ **Total Number of Sets**

IGNORING COPYRIGHT LAWS CAN BE A
$1,000,000 mistake!

Recent changes in the US copyright laws allow for statutory penalties of up to $150,000 per incident for copyright infringement involving any of the copyrighted plans found in this publication. The law can be confusing. So, for your own protection, take the time to understand what you cannot do when it comes to home plans.

WHAT YOU CAN'T DO!

YOU CANNOT DUPLICATE HOME PLANS

YOU CANNOT COPY ANY PART OF A HOME PLAN TO CREATE ANOTHER

YOU CANNOT BUILD A HOME WITHOUT BUYING A BLUEPRINT OR LICENSE

254 | DESIGNER DREAM HOMES

HOW TO ORDER BY PHONE, MAIL OR ONLINE

1-866-525-9374

Select the option that corresponds to the designer of your home plan:

Frank Betz Associates, dial 01
Donald A. Gardner Architects, dial 02
Dan Sater - Sater Design Collection, dial 03
Garrell Associates, dial 09
CornerStone Designs, dial 12

This puts you in DIRECT contact with the designer's office!

ADDITIONAL ITEMS**

Additional Blueprints (per set) $60.00
Full Reverse Set* $145.00

MATERIALS LIST*

Plan Categories A — E $75.00
Plan Categories F — O $80.00

FOUNDATION OPTIONS*

(basement, crawl space or slab, if different from base plan)
(no charge for Frank Betz plans, call designer for details)

Plan Categories A — C $225.00
Plan Categories D — E $250.00
Plan Categories F — M $275.00
Specification Outline* $15.00

*Call for availability. Special orders may require additional fees.

SHIPPING AND HANDLING

Overnight . . . . $45.00   Ground $22.00
2nd Day . . . . $35.00   Saturday $55.00

For shipping international, please call for a quote.

**Products and prices vary for each designer. Call for specific availability and pricing.

BLUEPRINT PRICE SCHEDULE*

	1 STUDY** SET	5 SETS	8 SETS	VELLUM	CD SET
A	$480	$535	$590	$730	$1460
B	$525	$580	$635	$795	$1590
C	$570	$625	$680	$860	$1720
D	$615	$675	$725	$925	$1850
E	$660	$720	$770	$990	$1980
F	$705	$765	$815	$1055	$2110
G	$775	$835	$885	$1135	$2270
H	$850	$910	$960	$1215	$2430
I	$950	$1010	$1060	$1315	$2630
J	$1050	$1110	$1160	$1415	$2830
K	$1150	$1210	$1260	$1515	$3030
L	$1250	$1310	$1360	$1615	$3230
M	$1350	$1410	$1460	$1715	$3430
N	$1450	$1510	$1560	$1815	$3630
O	Call for pricing				

* Prices subject to change without notice

** Call for availability

Order Form

PLAN NUMBER _____

☐ 1-set [study only] . . . . $_____
☐ 4-set building package . . . . $_____
☐ 8-set building package . . . . $_____
☐ 1-set of reproducible vellums . . . . $_____

____ Additional Identical Blueprints @ $60 each $_____

____ Full Reverse Set @ $145 fee $_____

Foundation Options:

____ Crawl Space ____ Slab ____ Basement $_____
(no charge for Frank Betz plans)

Sub-Total $_____
Shipping and Handling $_____
Sales Tax *(will be determined upon placing order)* $_____

TOTAL $_____

Check one: ☐ Visa ☐ MasterCard

Credit Card Number _____

Expiration Date _____

Signature _____

Name _____

Company _____

Street _____

City _____ State____ Zip_____

Daytime Telephone Number (_____)_____

Check one:

☐ Consumer   ☐ Builder   ☐ Developer

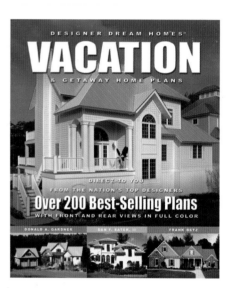
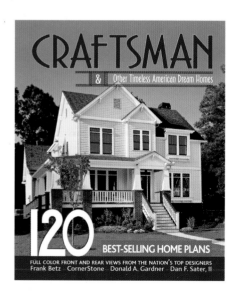